Collins

Step-Up

Name: ....

Class: ....

NEW MATHS FRAMEWORKING

Jeanette Mumford and Sandra Roberts

Contents

Understanding Number

1.1 Counting

- I can count to 50.

Key words
counting, numbers

Let's practise counting.
Get a pot of buttons.
Take out a handful.
Guess how many buttons you have.
Write down your guess.
Put your buttons in a line.
Count each button as you put it down.
Say the the number out loud.

Write the number down. [ ]

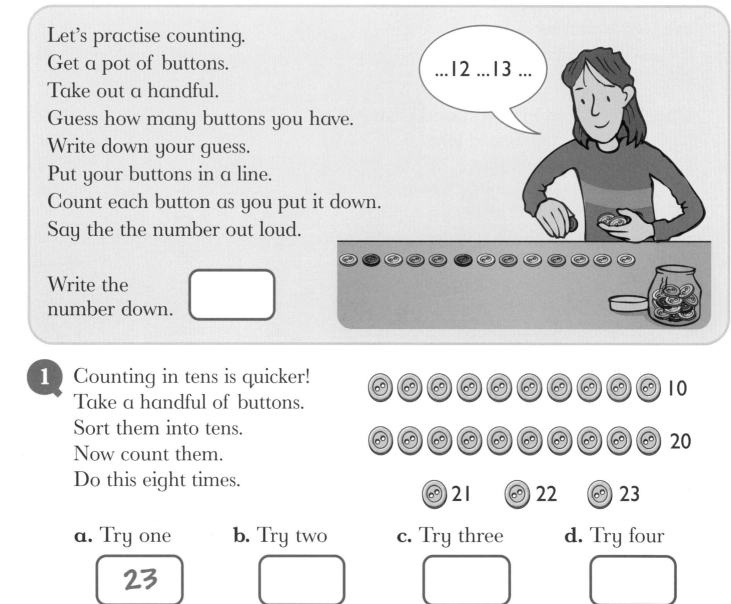

1 Counting in tens is quicker!
Take a handful of buttons.
Sort them into tens.
Now count them.
Do this eight times.

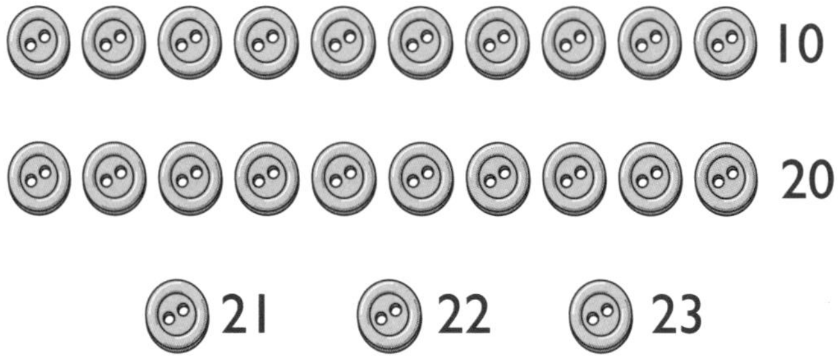

a. Try one	**b.** Try two	**c.** Try three	**d.** Try four
23			
e. Try five	**f.** Try six	**g.** Try seven	**h.** Try eight

2 Look at these buttons. Count in tens then ones.
How many buttons are there?

a.  ☐

b. 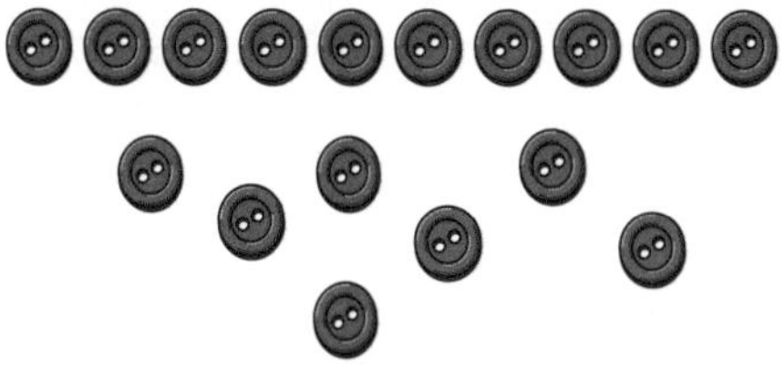 ☐

c. 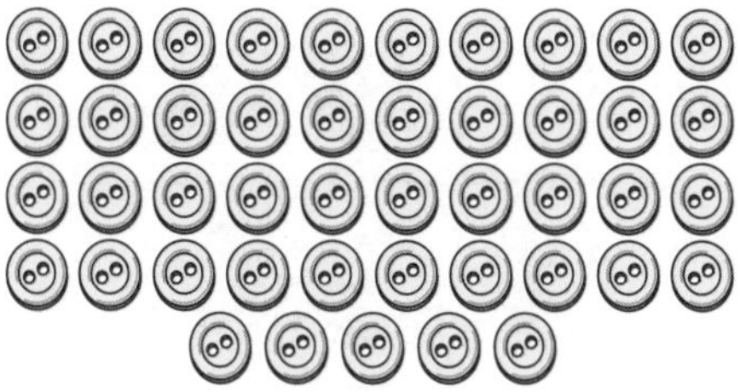 ☐

d. 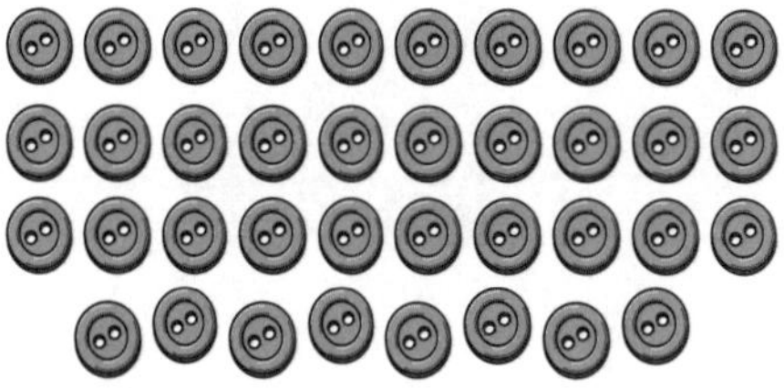 ☐

e. 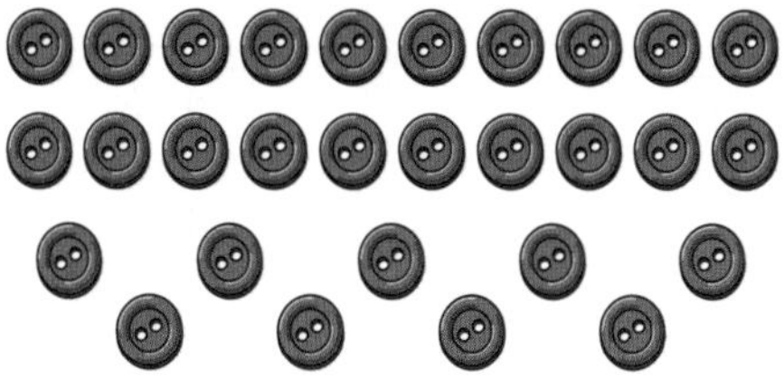 ☐

f.  ☐

3 Write the numbers from 1 to 50 in this grid.

1	2								
									50

◆ I can count to 50. ☐

Let's try this!

Counting backwards

Take out a handful of buttons. Put them in a line.
Count them forwards. Then count them backwards.

1.2 Place value

- I can understand two digit numbers.

Key words
digit, tens, ones

Two digit numbers have tens and ones.

Tens numbers

10 20 30 40 50

60 70 80 90 100

Ones numbers

1 2 3 4 5

6 7 8 9

1 Say these numbers.

10 11 12 13 14 15 16 17 18 19 20

Write the correct numbers under each picture.

a. 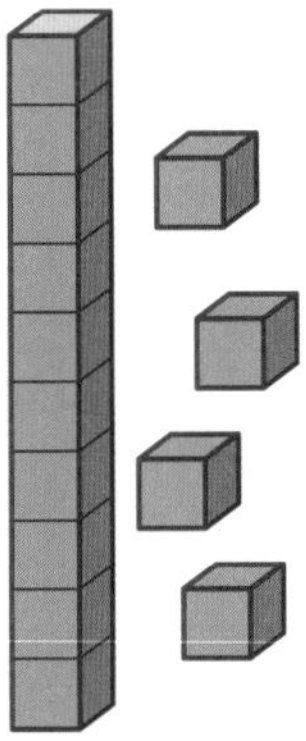

b. 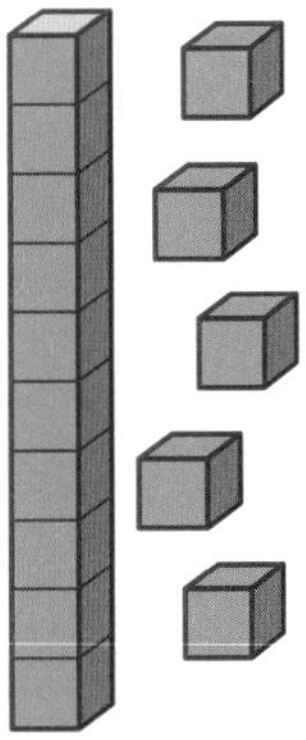

c. 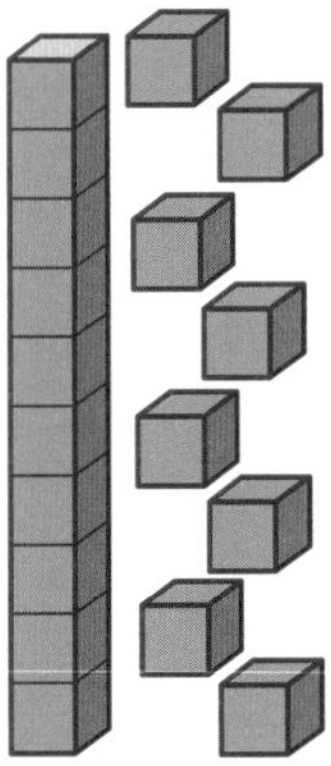

d. 

e. 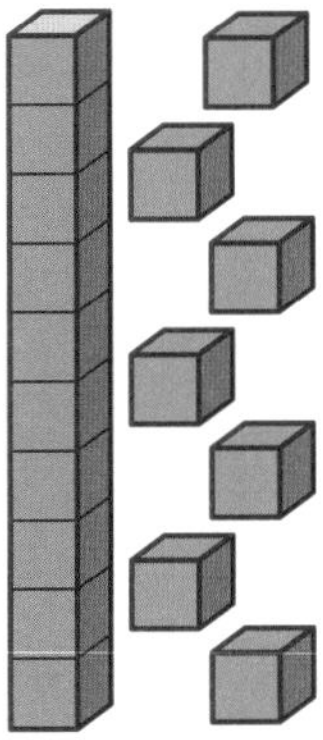

f. 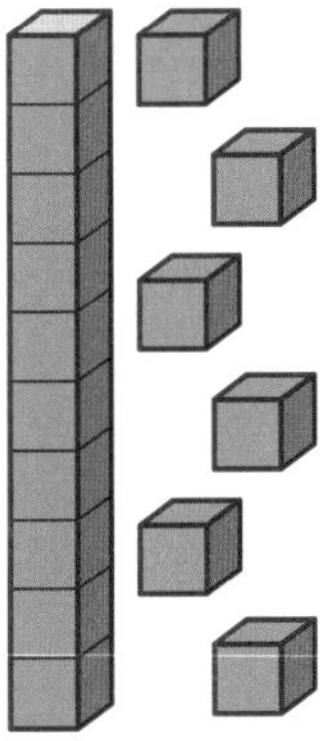

a.	b.	c.	d.	e.	f.
14					

g.

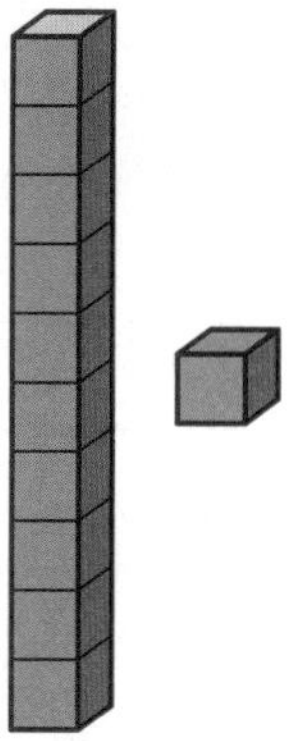

h.

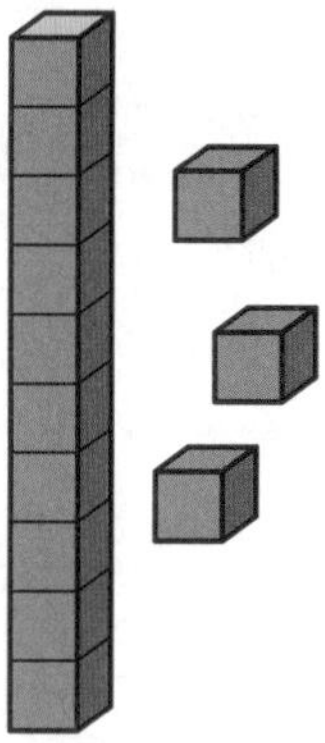

i.

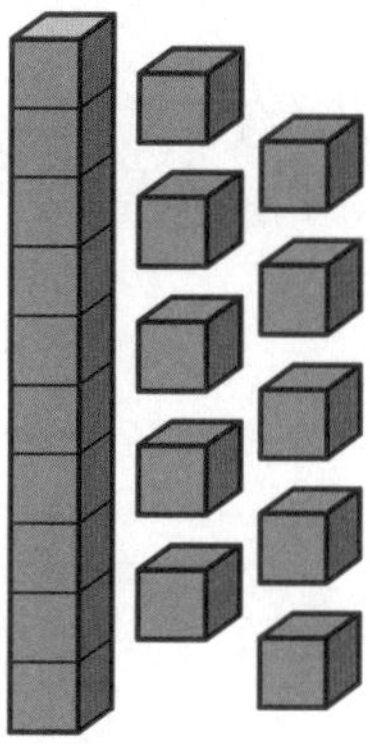

j.

k.

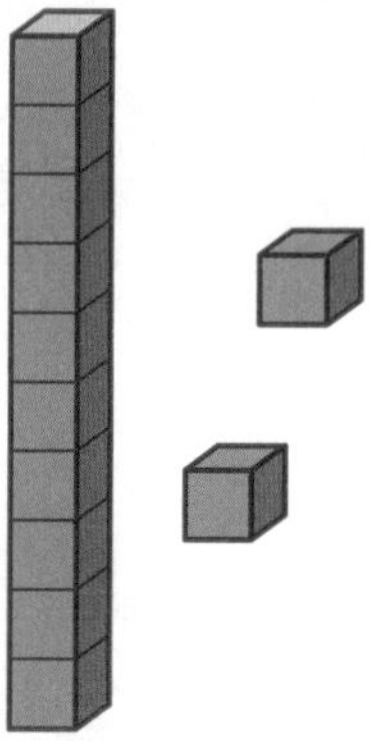

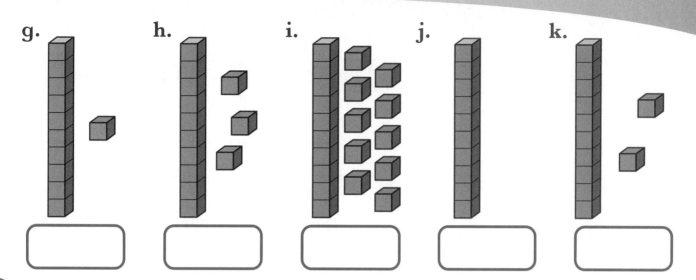

2 Draw the tens and ones pictures for these numbers.
Then, write the tens number and the ones number in the boxes.

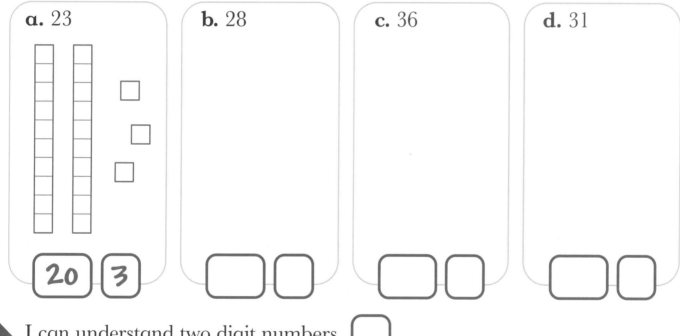

a. 23

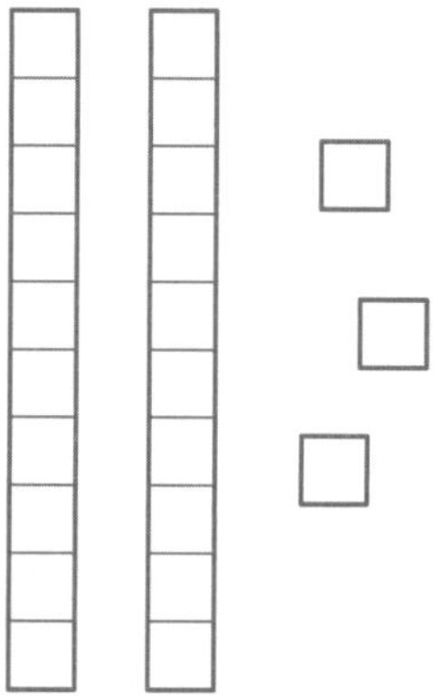

20 | 3

b. 28

c. 36

d. 31

I can understand two digit numbers.

Let's try this!

Look at the numbers in the two clouds.
Use them to make as many two digit numbers as you can.

Can you make all nine numbers?

1.3 Ordering numbers

- I can order numbers to 50.

Key words
higher, lower, order, smallest, largest

Here is a game to order numbers.
You will need 1–50 cards.
Pick any card. Call out the number.
Say, 'higher' or 'lower'.
Your partner says a number that is higher or lower than your number.
If the answer is correct, your partner keeps the card.
Now it is your partner's turn to pick a card.

1 Look at these cards.
Write a number **higher** than the number on the cards.

a. 17 ☐ b. 23 ☐ c. 46 ☐ d. 39 ☐ e. 8 ☐ f. 25 ☐

2 Now look at these cards.
Write a number **lower** than the number on the cards.

a. 37 ☐ b. 50 ☐ c. 28 ☐ d. 31 ☐ e. 14 ☐ f. 42 ☐

3 Look at these cards.
Put the numbers in order from **smallest** to **largest**.

a. 4 15 28 17 6

4, 6, 15, 17, 28

b. 20 12 28 2 32

c. 48 12 23 36 19

d. 30 13 37 43 3

e. 41 14 40 10 44

f. 15 11 50 25 35

I can order numbers to 50. ☐

Let's try this!

Look at the numbers on these cards.
Use them to make 10 two digit numbers.
Now, put your two digit numbers in order from smallest to largest.

1 4 6 3 2

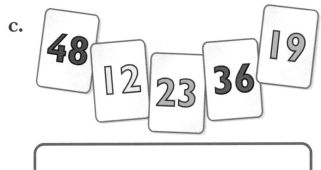

1.4 One more, one less

- I can say the number that is one more or one less.

Key words
more, next, less

Adam is saving money.
Each £1 coin is **one more** in his money box.
Every time he puts £1 in his money box, he circles the next number.

1 2 3 4 5 6 7 8 9 10 11 12 13 14 15

1 Read the numbers on the cards.
Write the number that is **one more**.

a.	b.	c.	d.	e.	f.	g.	h.
16	23	38	12	43	15	47	31
17							

16 + 1 = 17

2 **One more** is the same as adding 1.
Write the number that is one more.

a. 13 + 1 = 14 **b.** 32 + 1 = ☐ **c.** 21 + 1 = ☐

d. 46 + 1 = ☐ **e.** 19 + 1 = ☐ **f.** 28 + 1 = ☐

g. 49 + 1 = ☐ **h.** 36 + 1 = ☐ **i.** 23 + 1 = ☐

3 Read the numbers on the cards.
Write the number that is **one less**.

a.	b.	c.	d.	e.	f.	g.	h.
18	20	37	10	48	49	33	25
17							

18 - 1 = 17

4 **One less** is the same as taking away 1.
Write the number that is one less.

a. 18 – 1 = 17 **b.** 37 – 1 = ☐ **c.** 26 – 1 = ☐

d. 41 – 1 = ☐ **e.** 24 – 1 = ☐ **f.** 33 – 1 = ☐

g. 48 – 1 = ☐ **h.** 45 – 1 = ☐ **i.** 29 – 1 = ☐

◆ I can say the number that is one more or one less. ☐

Let's try this!

Look at these numbers.

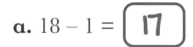

12 36 41 29 8 30 44 50

Write the numbers that are **two more**.
Write the numbers that are **two less**.

1.5 10 more, 10 less

- I can say the number that is 10 more or 10 less.

Key words
more, less

10 more or 10 less make a pattern.
The ones digit stays the same.
Only the tens number changes.
Count in tens starting from four.
Say the numbers out loud.

Number grid

1	2	3	(4)	5	6	7	8	9	10
11	12	13	(14)	15	16	17	18	19	20
21	22	23	(24)	25	26	27	28	29	30
31	32	33	(34)	35	36	37	38	39	40
41	42	43	(44)	45	46	47	48	49	50

1 Read the numbers on the cards.
Write the number that is 10 more.
Use the number grid to help you.

a.	b.	c.	d.	e.	f.	g.	h.
14	21	29	10	46	13	35	42
24							

14 + 10 = 24

2 **10 more** is the same as adding 10.
Write the number that is 10 more.

a. 16 + 10 = 26 **b.** 35 + 10 = ☐ **c.** 24 + 10 = ☐

d. 44 + 10 = ☐ **e.** 22 + 10 = ☐ **f.** 31 + 10 = ☐

3 Read the numbers on the cards.
Write the number that is 10 less.

a.	b.	c.	d.	e.	f.	g.	h.
17	28	40	39	11	45	23	19
7							

17 − 10 = 7

4 **10 less** is the same as taking away 10.
Write the number that is 10 less.

a. 19 − 10 = 9 b. 33 − 10 = ☐ c. 21 − 10 = ☐

d. 37 − 10 = ☐ e. 29 − 10 = ☐ f. 35 − 10 = ☐

g. 44 − 10 = ☐ h. 41 − 10 = ☐ i. 28 − 10 = ☐

◆ I can say the number that is 10 more or 10 less. ☐

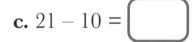

Let's try this!

1. Pick one of these numbers.
   Write it down.
   Add on 10 as many times as you can.
   Write down the numbers.

   7 3 5 1

2. Pick one of these numbers.
   Write it down.
   Take away 10 as many times as you can.
   Write down the numbers.

   42 50 45 49

Addition

2.1 Understanding addition

- I can understand addition.

Key words
add, equals, altogether, more, bigger

If you add two numbers together, you get more.

The answer will be bigger.

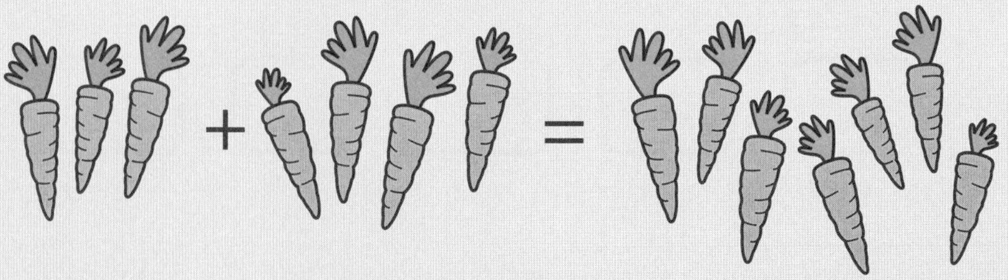

3 carrots and 4 carrots make 7 carrots

3 plus 4 equals 7

$3 + 4 = 7$

1 Get two dice. Roll them and count the dots on each dice.
Write them down as an addition sum.
Do this 12 times.

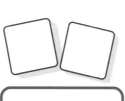

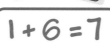

a. 

1 + 6 = 7

b.

c.

d.

e.

f.

g.

h.

i.

j.

k.

l.

2 Look at the pictures of cakes. There are cherries on each cake.
How many cherries are there altogether?
Write this down as an addition sum.

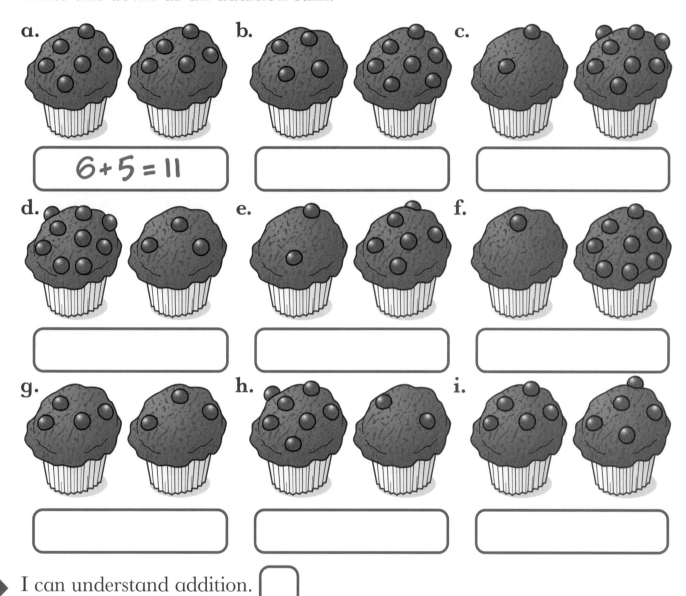

a.

6+5 = 11

b.

c.

d.

e.

f.

g.

h.

i.

I can understand addition. ☐

Let's try this!

You will need some number cards and buttons.

Take out a number card and some buttons.
Say the number on the card aloud.
Now count on the number of buttons.
Write this down.
Write an addition sum.

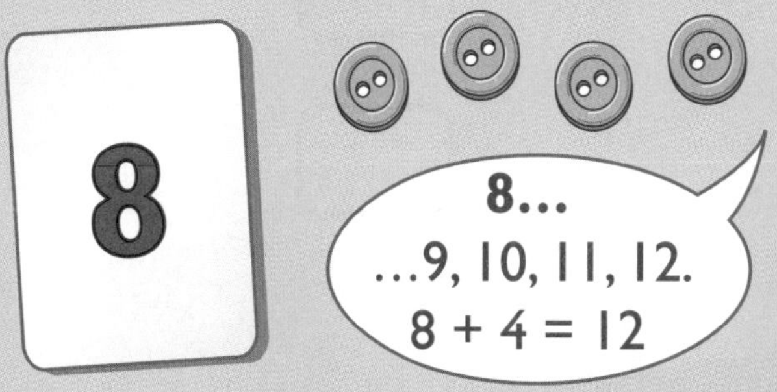

2.2 Adding with a number line (1)

- I can add using a number line.

Key words
add, equals, order

A number line helps you to add
Keep your finger on the first number you need to add.
Now jump as many times as the second number.

Put your finger on 8. Count on 7 jumps.
Did you land on 15?
8 coconuts add 7 coconuts equals 15 coconuts.

1 Use the number line to add these numbers.
Remember, start by putting your finger on the first number.

a. 5 + 4 = 9 **b.** 9 + 6 = ☐ **c.** 7 + 4 = ☐

d. 8 + 3 = ☐ **e.** 9 + 5 = ☐ **f.** 10 + 7 = ☐

g. 13 + 5 = ☐ **h.** 11 + 4 = ☐ **i.** 15 + 5 = ☐

j. 14 + 3 = ☐ **k.** 9 + 9 = ☐ **l.** 17 + 2 = ☐

2 You can add in any order.
Start from the biggest number.
This makes adding easier.
Circle the biggest number in each of these sums.
Then add them using the number line on page 16.

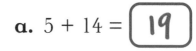

3 + 2 = 5

2 + 3 = 5

a. 5 + 14 = 19   **b.** 12 + 4 = ☐   **c.** 7 + 11 = ☐

d. 6 + 13 = ☐   **e.** 16 + 3 = ☐   **f.** 9 + 10 = ☐

g. 2 + 17 = ☐   **h.** 5 + 13 = ☐   **i.** 7 + 8 = ☐

j. 4 + 13 = ☐   **k.** 8 + 9 = ☐   **l.** 15 + 2 = ☐

3 Why is it better to start with the biggest number? Write your answer in the box.

☐

◆ I can add using a number line. ☐

Let's try this!

You will need a 0–30 number line.
Look at the bags of marbles.
Choose a number from each bag.
Make 10 addition sums.
Work them out using the 0–30 number line.

2.3 Adding with a number line (2)

- I can add bigger numbers using a number line.

Key words
add, equals

A number line helps you to add.
You can use a number line to add bigger numbers.
Look at the numbers you need to add.

21 + 8 = ?

Put your finger on the biggest number: 21. Count on 8 jumps.
Did you land on 29?
21 coconuts add 8 coconuts equals 29 coconuts.

1 Use the number line to add these numbers.
Remember, start by putting your finger on the biggest number.

a. 25 + 6 = 31 **b.** 29 + 4 = ☐ **c.** 21 + 8 = ☐

d. 24 + 10 = ☐ **e.** 27 + 5 = ☐ **f.** 26 + 11 = ☐

g. 22 + 15 = ☐ **h.** 20 + 14 = ☐ **i.** 32 + 6 = ☐

j. 34 + 3 = ☐ **k.** 29 + 11 = ☐ **l.** 35 + 2 = ☐

2 Look at the numbers on the coconuts.
Write addition sums for each pair of coconuts.
Add them using a number line.

a.

24 + 7 = 31

b.

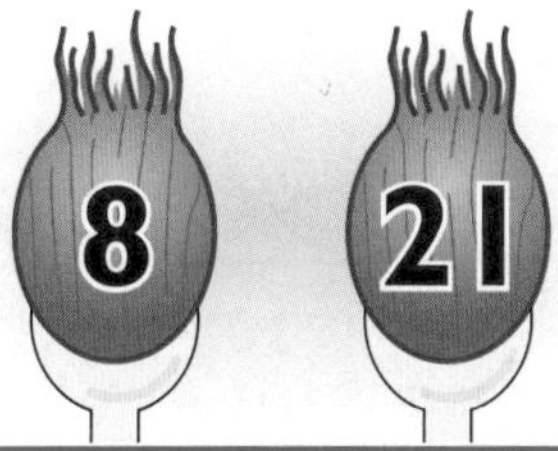

c.

d.

e.

f.

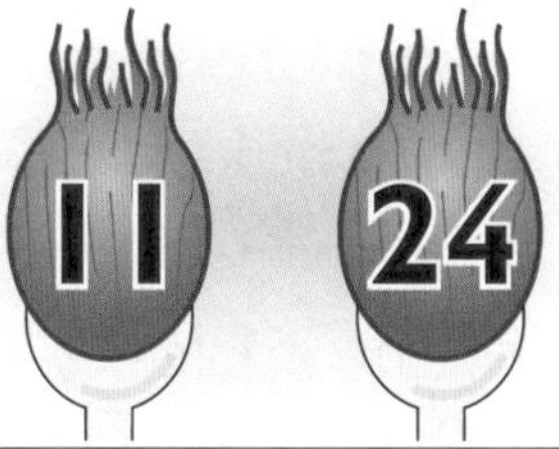

g.

h.

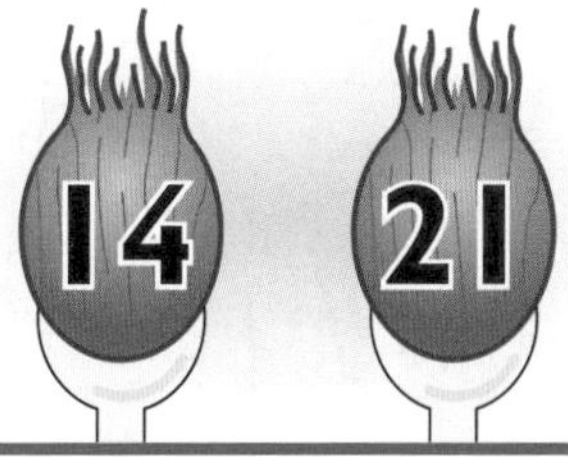

i.

I can add bigger numbers using a number line. ☐

Let's try this!

Remember the number 15.
Add these numbers to 15
by counting on.

a. 4 **b.** 6 **c.** 9
d. 10 **e.** 8 **f.** 13

2.4 Addition facts for 10

- I know the addition facts for the number 10.

Key words
addition, facts, double

There are 10 marbles altogether.
Five are on the table. The rest are in the pot.

How many are in the pot? ☐

Try to remember the pairs of numbers that make 10.
Use some marbles to help you learn addition facts for 10.

1 Fill in the missing numbers on the empty cards to make 10.

a. b. c. d. e. f.

2 Get out nine cubes.
In how many different ways can you make 9?

Use your cubes to find out the missing numbers.

9

a. 6 + 3 b. ☐ + ☐ c. ☐ + ☐

d. ☐ + ☐ e. ☐ + ☐ f. ☐ + ☐

3 Fill in the answers to these questions as quickly as you can.

a. 3 + 4 = 7 **b.** 2 + 3 = ☐ **c.** 1 + 6 = ☐

d. 5 + 3 = ☐ **e.** 7 + 3 = ☐ **f.** 4 + 2 = ☐

g. 7 + 2 = ☐ **h.** 4 + 6 = ☐ **i.** 5 + 2 = ☐

j. 6 + 3 = ☐ **k.** 5 + 4 = ☐ **l.** 9 + 1 = ☐

4 Double these numbers.
Write the sum to go with it.

a. Double 2 is 4

2 + 2 = 4

b. Double 5 is ☐

c. Double 1 is ☐

d. Double 3 is ☐

e. Double 4 is ☐

f. Double 0 is ☐

◆ I know the addition facts for the number 10. ☐

Let's try this!

Get two dice.
Roll them. Add the two numbers.
Write down the addition sum.

2.5 Addition facts for 20

- I know the addition facts for the number 20.

Key words
addition, facts

Look at the 20 stars.
Count them aloud as
'5…10…15…20'

The stars can help you to learn addition facts for the number 20.

15 + 5 = 20

1 Look at the dots.
Write the addition facts that they show.

a.

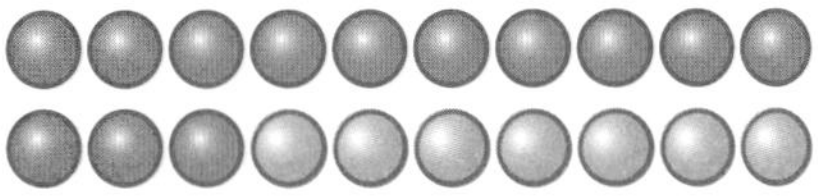

13 + 7 = 20

b.

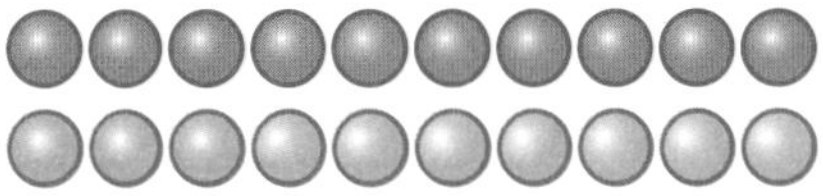

c.

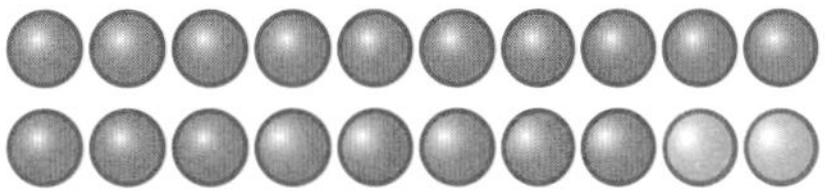

d.

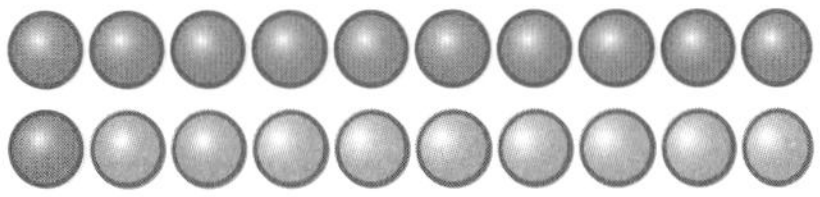

e.

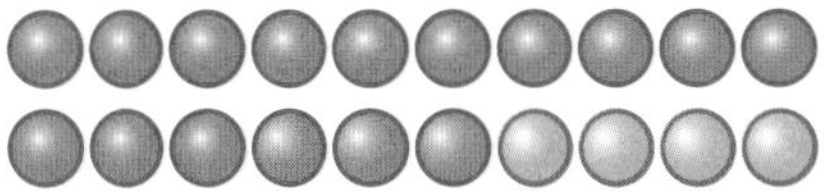

f.

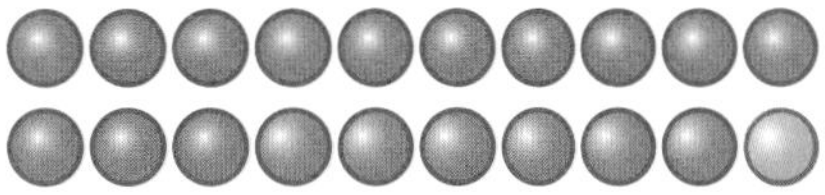

g.

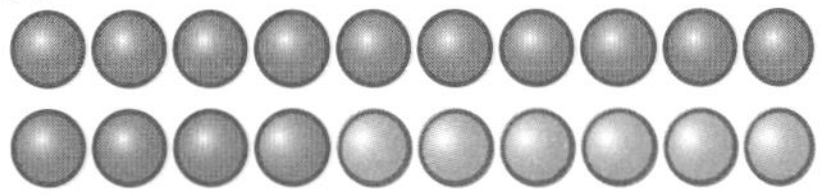

h.

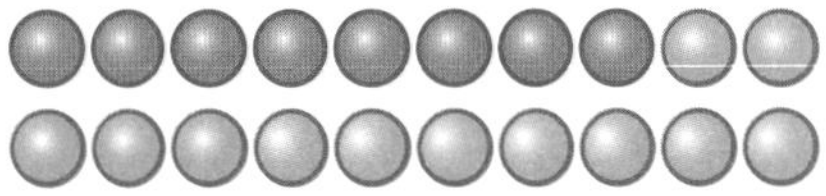

i.

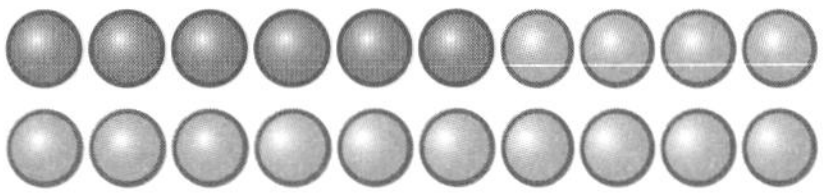

2 Try and remember the pairs of numbers that make 20.
The number and the missing number should add up to 20.
Write the missing numbers as quickly as you can.

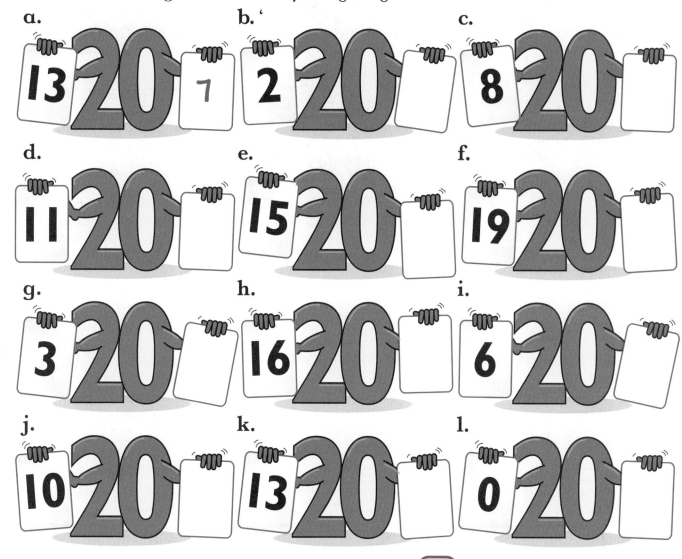

a. 13 20 7	**b.** 2 20 ___	**c.** 8 20 ___
d. 11 20 ___	**e.** 15 20 ___	**f.** 19 20 ___
g. 3 20 ___	**h.** 16 20 ___	**i.** 6 20 ___
j. 10 20 ___	**k.** 13 20 ___	**l.** 0 20 ___

◆ I know the addition facts for the number 20. ☐

Let's try this!

You will need 0–20 number cards.
Mix up the cards.
Put them face down on the table.
Pick up a card.
What number goes with it to make 20?
Write down the sum.
Now pick another card.

SUBTRACTION

3.1 Understanding subtraction

- I can understand subtraction.

Key words
subtract, take away, equals, smaller

Subtracting means taking something away.
The answer is smaller.

9 take away 4 is 5.

1 You need 20 buttons, a dice and a jar.
Put all the buttons in the jar.
Take out at least six buttons.
Roll the dice.
Take away this number of buttons.
Write down your subtractions.
Put the buttons back into the jar.
Do this nine times.

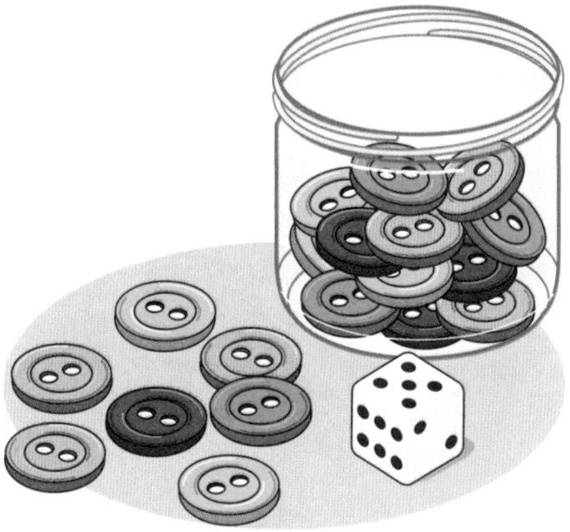

a. 7 buttons 

7-5=2

b. ☐ buttons ☐

☐

c. ☐ buttons ☐

☐

d. ☐ buttons ☐

☐

e. ☐ buttons ☐

☐

f. ☐ buttons ☐

☐

g. ☐ buttons ☐

☐

h. ☐ buttons ☐

☐

i. ☐ buttons ☐

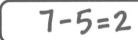

☐

2 Use buttons to work out these subtractions.
Get as many buttons as the first number.

Take away as many buttons as the second number.
How many are left?
Count them.

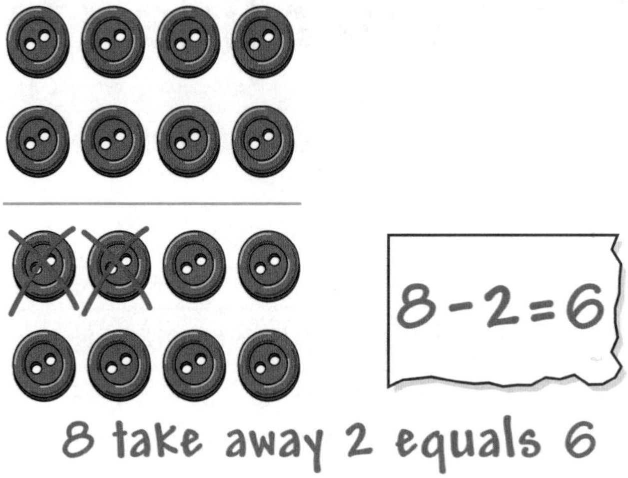

a. 8 – 2 = 6	**b.** 8 – 1 = ☐	**c.** 7 – 5 = ☐
d. 10 – 3 = ☐	**e.** 12 – 6 = ☐	**f.** 9 – 5 = ☐
g. 13 – 4 = ☐	**h.** 8 – 5 = ☐	**i.** 14 – 8 = ☐
j. 15 – 7 = ☐	**k.** 9 – 4 = ☐	**l.** 6 – 1 = ☐
m. 11 – 7 = ☐	**n.** 4 – 3 = ☐	**o.** 15 – 5 = ☐

◆ I can understand subtraction. ☐

Let's try this!

You will need 1–9 number cards and some buttons.
Get two number cards.
Use them to write a subtraction.
Use the number cards to do 10 more subtractions.
Use the buttons to work out the answers.

3.2 Subtracting with a number line (1)

- I can subtract using a number line.

Key words
subtract, equals

A number line helps you to subtract.
Start by keeping your finger on the first number.
Look at the number you need to subtract.
Jump back that many times.

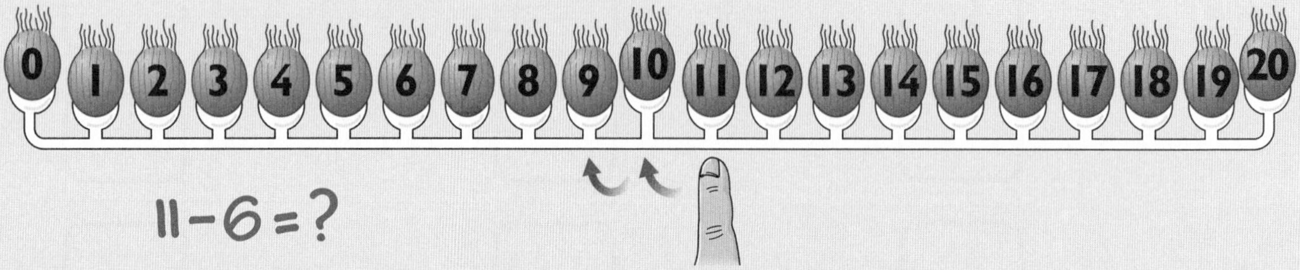

Put your finger on the number 11. Jump back 6 times.
Did you land on 5?
11 coconuts subtract 6 coconuts equals 5 coconuts.

1 Use the number line to subtract these numbers.
Remember, start by keeping your finger on the first number.

a. 11 – 3 = 8 **b.** 8 – 2 = ☐ **c.** 12 – 5 = ☐

d. 13 – 7 = ☐ **e.** 10 – 6 = ☐ **f.** 14 – 7 = ☐

g. 9 – 9 = ☐ **h.** 12 – 8 = ☐ **i.** 15 – 2 = ☐

j. 17 – 5 = ☐ **k.** 19 – 8 = ☐ **l.** 18 – 8 = ☐

2 Subtracting cannot be done in any order. The biggest number must be first.

5 – 2 =

I can take away 2 and there will be 3 left.
✓

2 – 5 =

I cannot take away 5 from 2!
✗

Look at these subtractions. Which ones can be done?
Tick the ones that can be done.
Cross the ones that cannot be done.
Use a number line to work out the ones you have ticked.

a. ✓ 11 – 3 = 8 **b.** 10 – 5 = ☐ **c.** 9 – 2 = ☐

d. 6 – 9 = ☐ **e.** 11 – 7 = ☐ **f.** 10 – 13 = ☐

g. 15 – 4 = ☐ **h.** 16 – 9 = ☐ **i.** 12 – 20 = ☐

3 Why does the biggest number have to come first in subtraction? Write your answer in the box.

◆ I can subtract using a number line. ☐

Let's try this!

You will need a 0–30 number line.

Look at the numbers in the bags.
Choose a number from each bag.
Make up 10 subtractions.

3.3 Subtracting with a number line (2)

- I can subtract bigger numbers using a number line.

Key words
subtract, equals

A number line helps you to subtract.
You can use a number line to subtract bigger numbers.

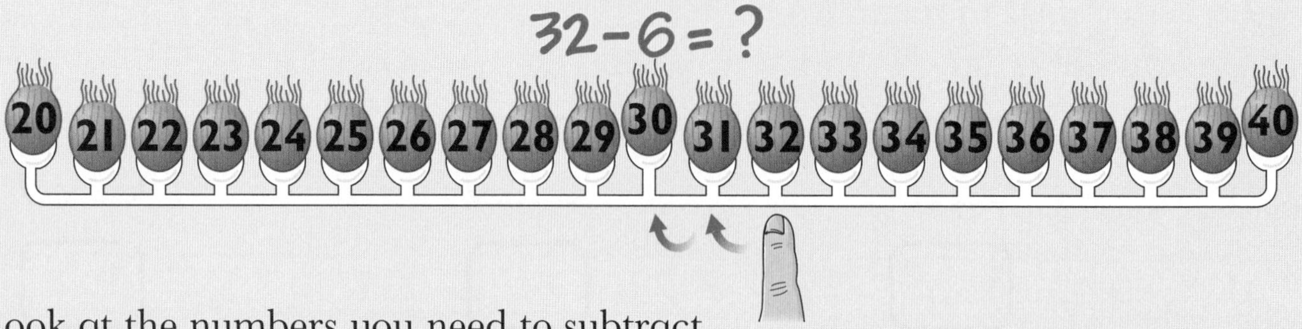

Look at the numbers you need to subtract.
Put your finger on the biggest number.
Jump back as many times as the other number.
Did you land on 26?
32 coconuts subtract 6 coconuts equals 26 coconuts.

1 Use the number line to subtract these numbers.
Remember, start by keeping your finger on the biggest number.

a. 35 – 4 = [31] **b.** 28 – 4 = [ ] **c.** 33 – 5 = [ ]

d. 26 – 2 = [ ] **e.** 30 – 7 = [ ] **f.** 35 – 8 = [ ]

g. 40 – 5 = [ ] **h.** 38 – 7 = [ ] **i.** 31 – 9 = [ ]

j. 37 – 11 = [ ] **k.** 35 – 6 = [ ] **l.** 30 – 10 = [ ]

2 Look at the numbers on the coconuts.
Write a subtraction for each pair of coconuts.

a.

29 − 6 = 23

b.
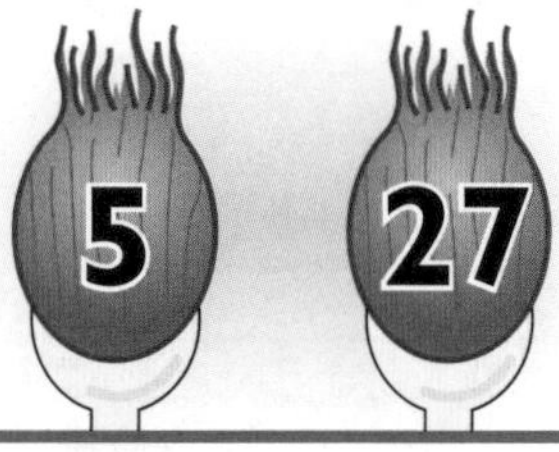

c.
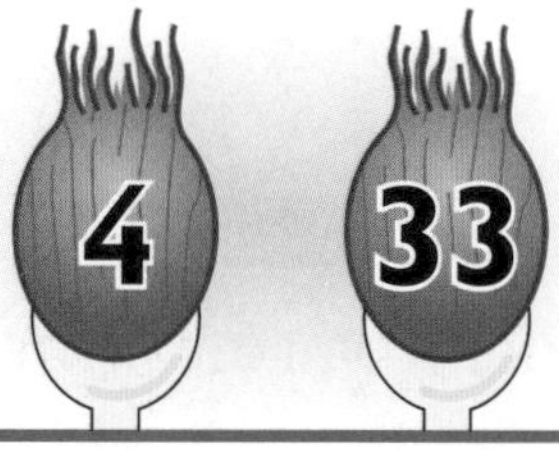

d.
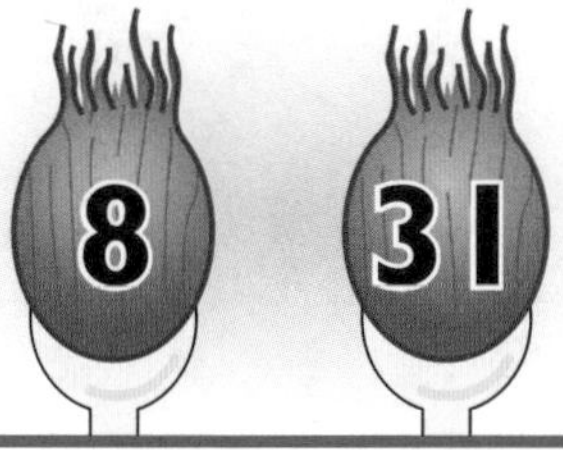

e.
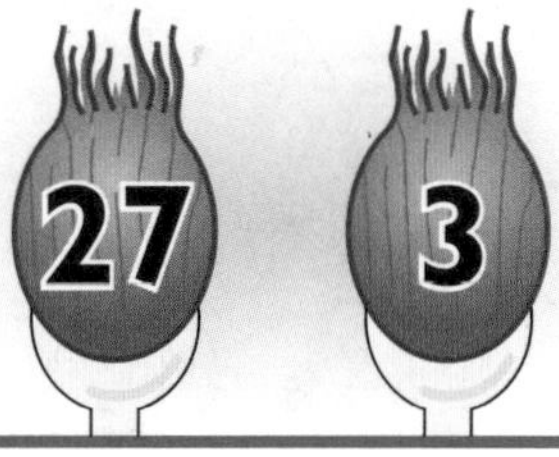

f.
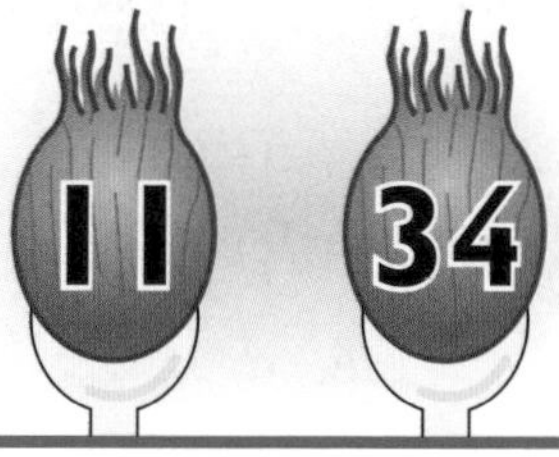

g.
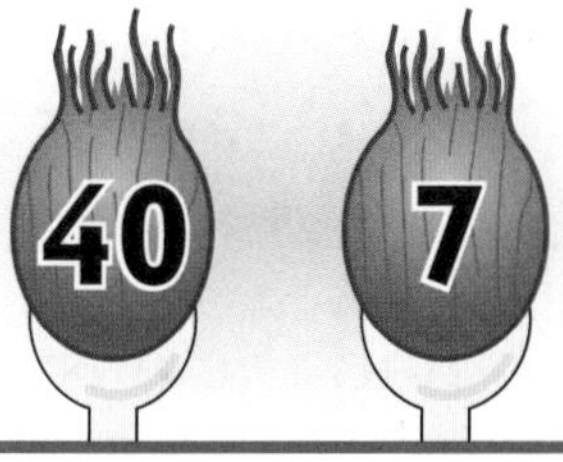

h.
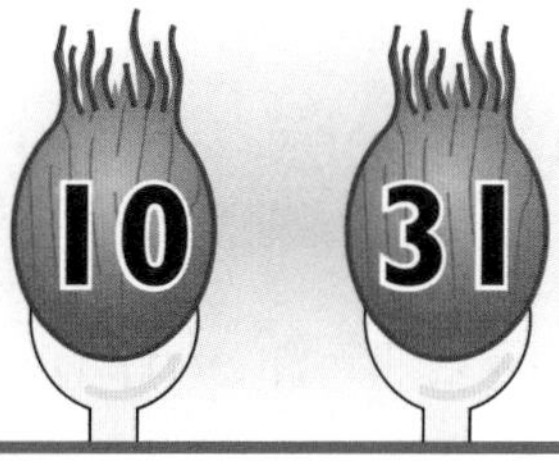

i.

j.
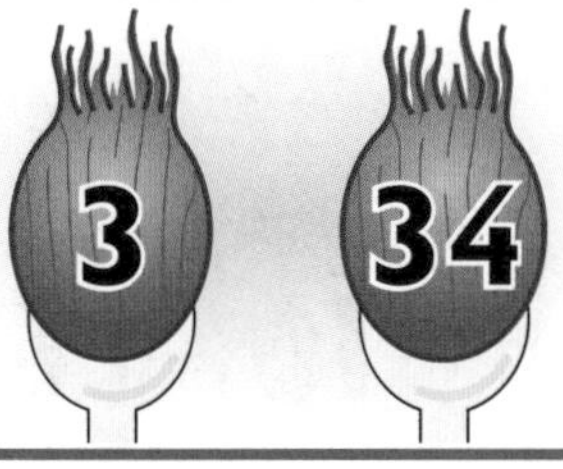

k.
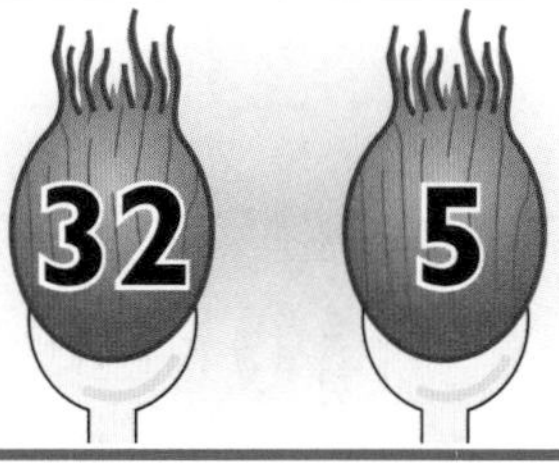

l.
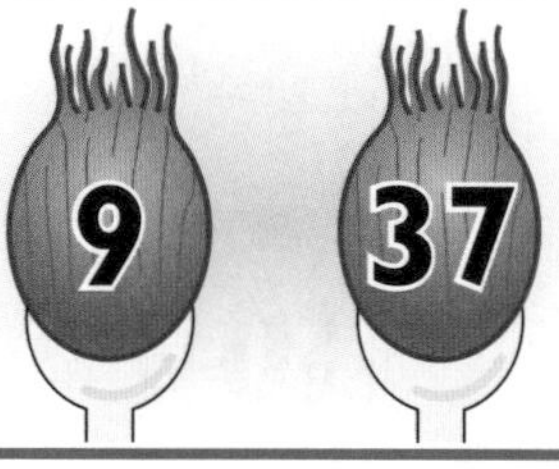

◆ I can subtract bigger numbers using a number line. ☐

Let's try this!

Draw your own number line from 20–40.
Then write 10 subtractions. Work them out.

3.4 Subtraction facts for 10

- I know the subtraction facts for the number 10.

Key words
subtraction, facts

There were 10 marbles in the pot.
Two were taken out and put on the table.

How many are left in the pot? ☐

Try to remember the subtraction facts for 10.
Use marbles to help you learn them.

How many marbles do you take away to leave 6 in the pot? ☐

1 Fill in the missing numbers. You can use marbles to find the answers.

a. 10 − 5 = 5
b. 10 − 3 = ☐
c. 10 − ☐ = 10

d. 10 − 1 = ☐
e. 10 − ☐ = 9
f. 10 − 6 = ☐

g. 10 − 2 = ☐
h. 10 − ☐ = 7
i. 10 − 4 = ☐

j. 10 − 8 = ☐
k. 10 − 7 = ☐
l. 10 − 0 = ☐

2 Get out five cubes.

Use them to work out the missing numbers.

a. 5 – 3 = 2 **b.** 5 – ☐ = ☐ **c.** 5 – ☐ = ☐

d. 5 – ☐ = ☐ **e.** 5 – ☐ = ☐ **f.** 5 – ☐ = ☐

3 Fill in the answers to these questions.

a. 6 – 1 = 5 **b.** 9 – 2 = ☐ **c.** 4 – 1 = ☐

d. 7 – 3 = ☐ **e.** 10 – 6 = ☐ **f.** 8 – 1 = ☐

g. 6 – 3 = ☐ **h.** 5 – 5 = ☐ **i.** 8 – 7 = ☐

j. 9 – 5 = ☐ **k.** 3 – 2 = ☐ **l.** 7 – 5 = ☐

◆ I know the subtraction facts for the number 10. ☐

Let's try this!

Look at the numbers on the cards.

Use the numbers to make as many subtraction facts as you can.

3.5 Subtraction facts for 20

- I know the subtraction facts for the number 20.

Key words
subtraction, facts

Look at the 20 stars.
Count them aloud.

They helped with the addition facts.
Now you can use them for subtraction facts.

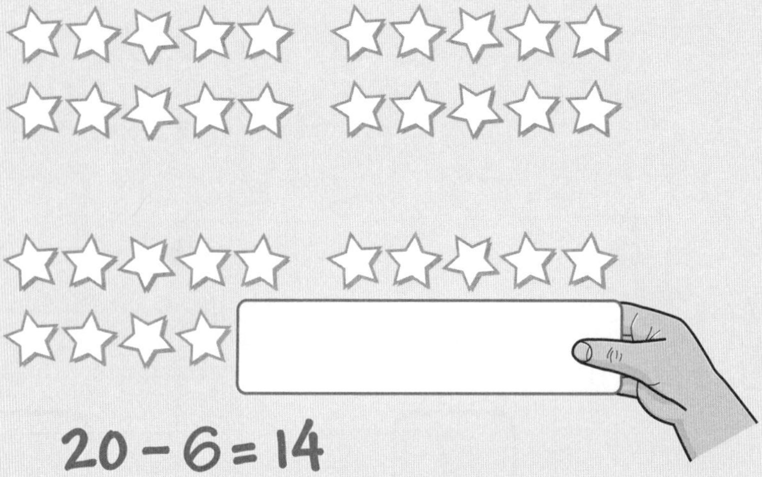

20 − 6 = 14

1 Look at the dots. Write the subtraction facts that they show.

a.

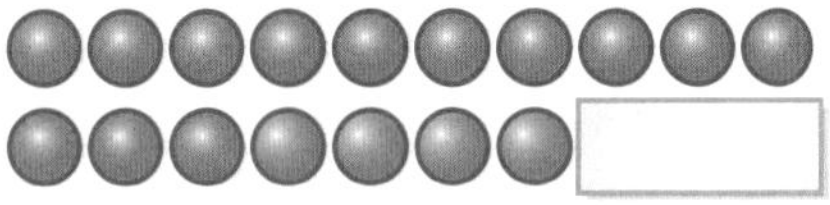

20 − 3 = 17

b.

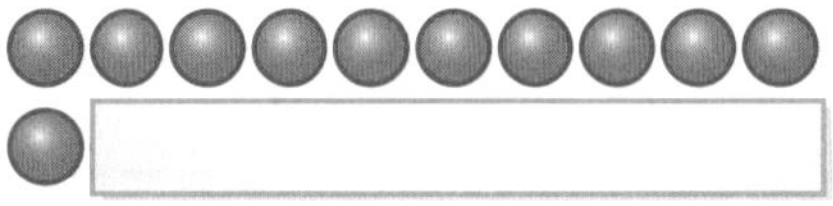

c.

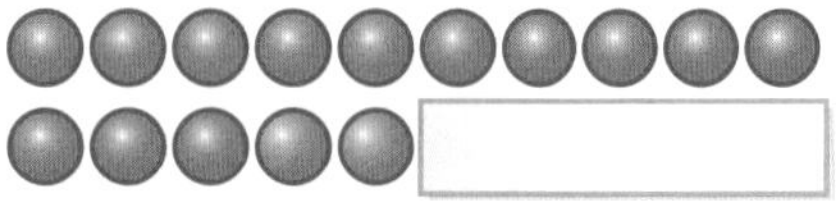

d.

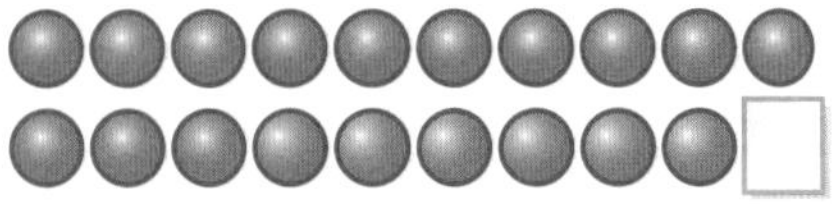

e.

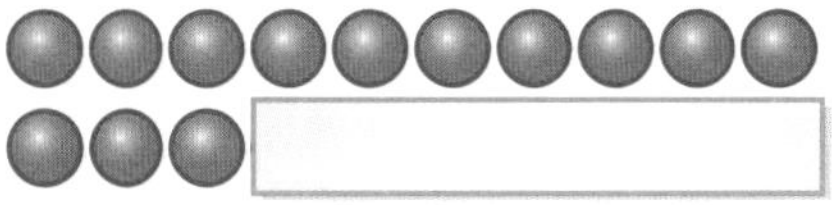

f.

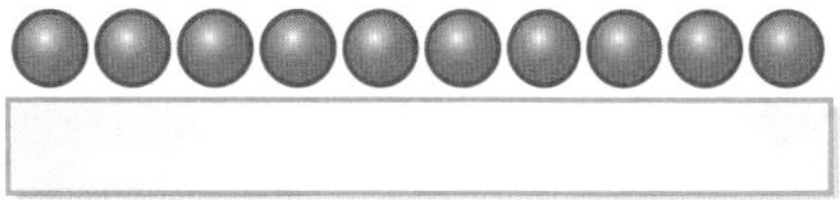

g.

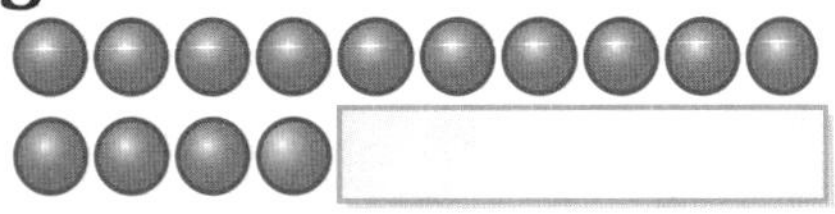

h.

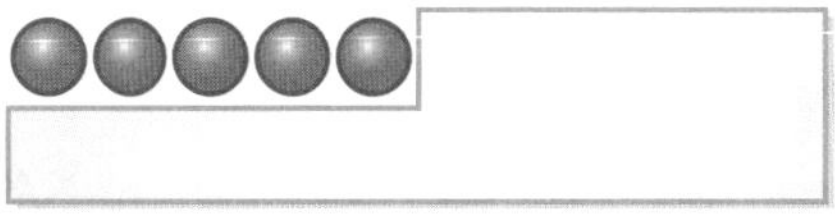

i.

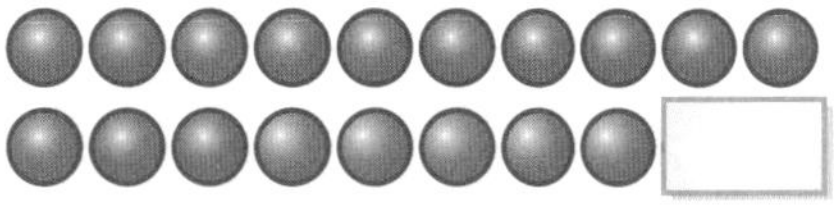

2 Look at the numbers that 20 is holding.
Use them to write two subtraction facts for 20.

a.

20 - 13 = 7
20 - 7 = 13

b.

c.

d.

e.

f.

g.

h.

i.

j.

◆ I know the subtraction facts for the number 20. ☐

Let's try this!

You will need 0–20 number cards.
Mix up the cards.
Put them face down on the table.
Pick up a card and look at the number.
Take it away from 20.
What is the answer? Write it down.
Now pick up other cards and do the same.

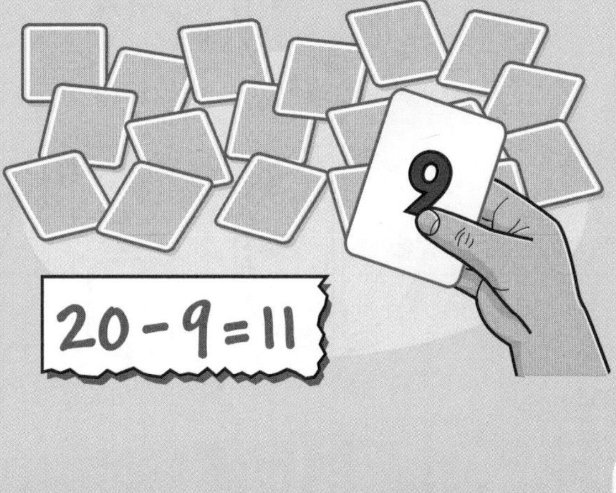

FRACTIONS

4.1 Understanding fractions

● I can understand halves.

Key words
fraction, half, share, same, equal, divide

A fraction is a part of something.
The parts must be the same.
Half is when two parts
are the same.

Get a paper and scissors.
How many ways can you cut
the sheet of paper in half?
Put the two parts together.
Are they the same?

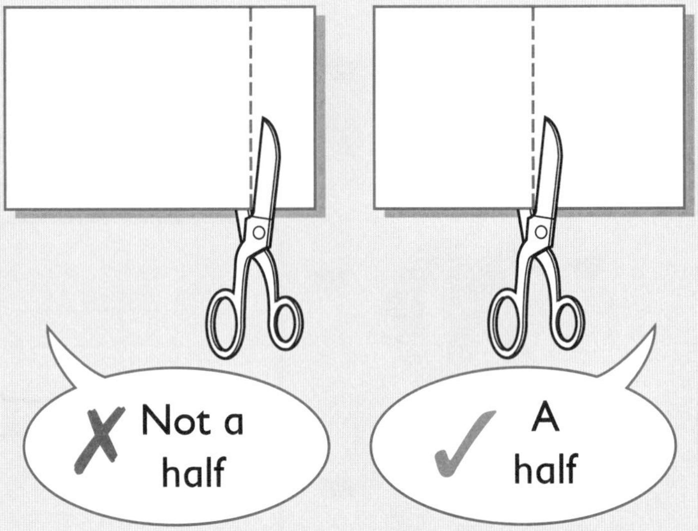

✗ Not a half

✓ A half

1 Jamila has been trying to cut some things in half.
Look at the pictures. Tick the ones that are halves.
Remember, to be half the **two** pieces must be the same (**equal**).

a. 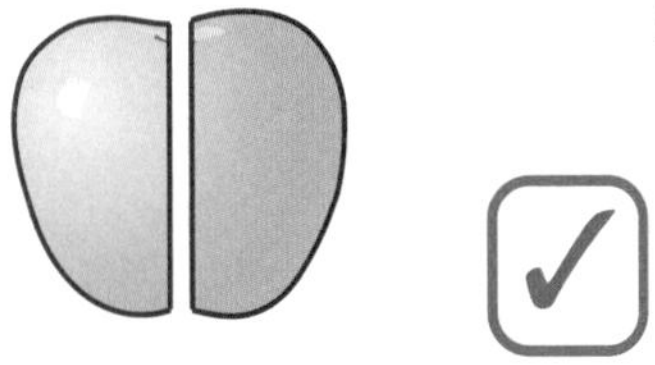 ✓

b.  ☐

c. 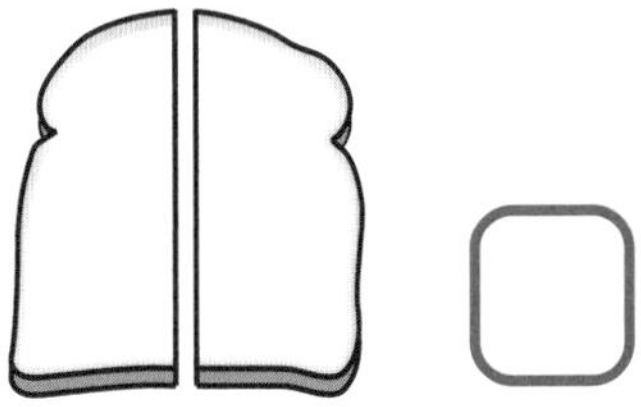 ☐

d. 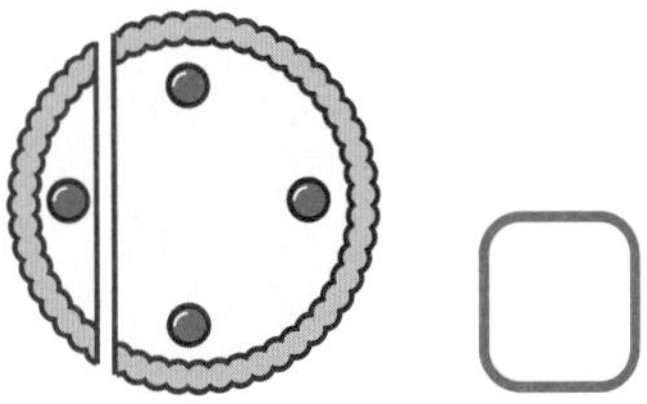 ☐

e. 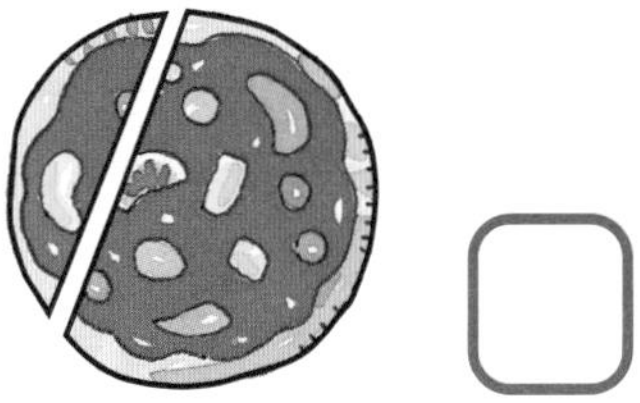 ☐

f. 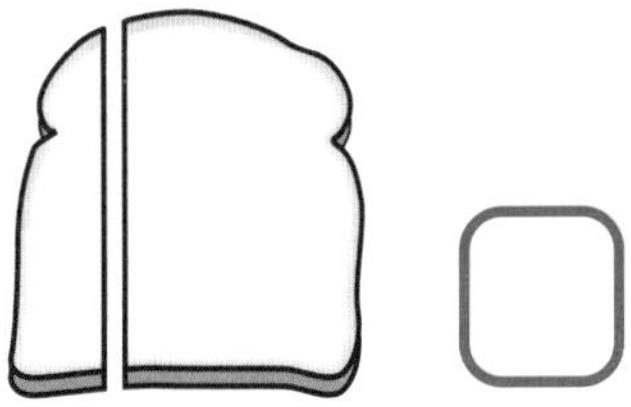 ☐

g. 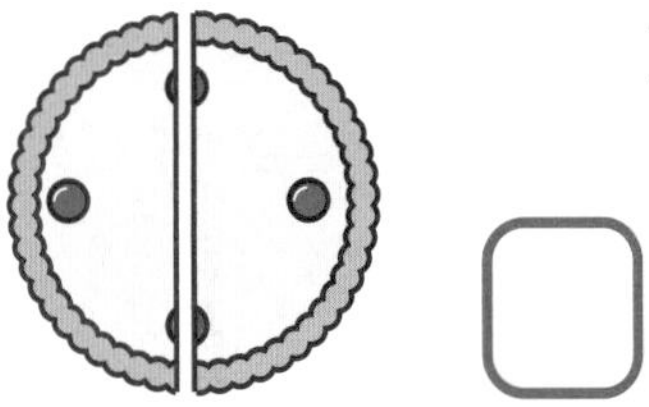 ☐

h.  ☐

i.  ☐

2 Draw a line to cut these things in half.

a.

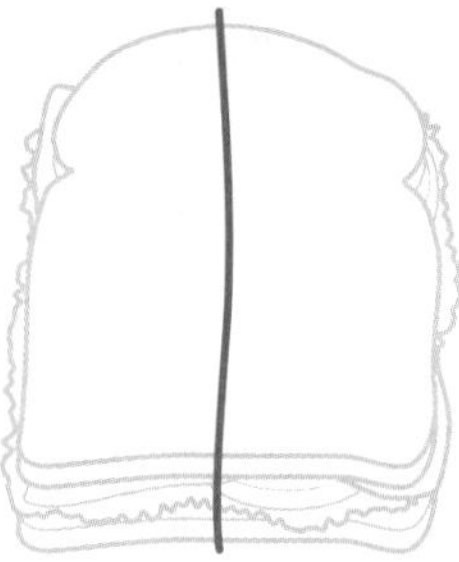

b.

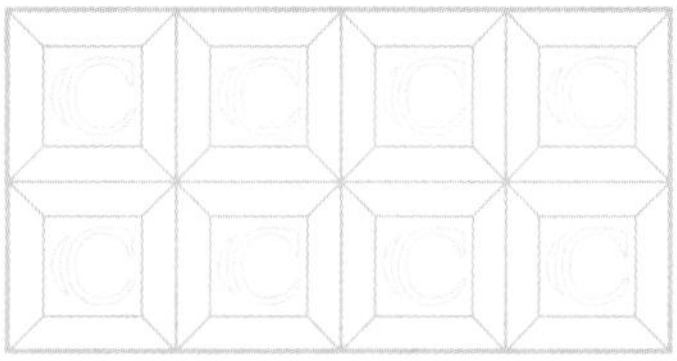

c.

d.

e.

f.

g.

h.

i.

j.

3 Draw a pizza.
Draw a line
to cut it
in half.

◆ I can divide an object into halves. ☐

Let's try this!

Draw an object and divide it in half.
Say what you did.

4.2 Halves of numbers

- I can halve a group of objects.

Key words
half, share, halve, equal, divide

Groups of things can be halved.
It is like sharing between two people.
The groups must be equal to be half.

Get two pots and 10 marbles.
Put half the marbles in one pot and half of them in the other pot.

1 Get some marbles and two pots.
Share the marbles between the two pots.

a. 6 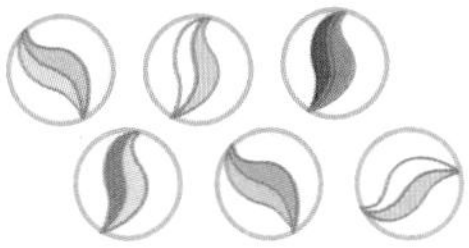 Half of 6 is [3]

b. 4 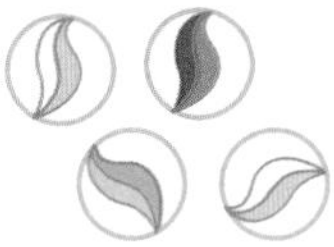 Half of 4 is [ ]

c. 8 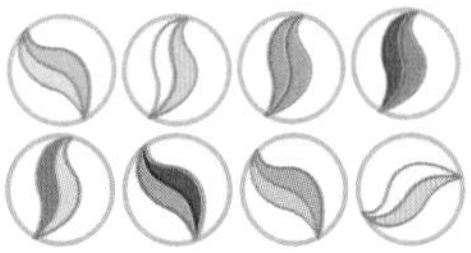 Half of 8 is [ ]

d. 2 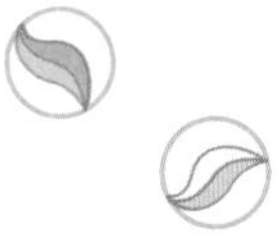 Half of 2 is [ ]

e. 14 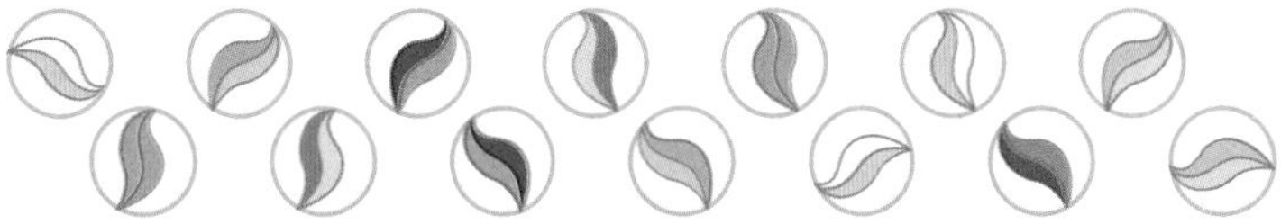 Half of 14 is [ ]

f. 16 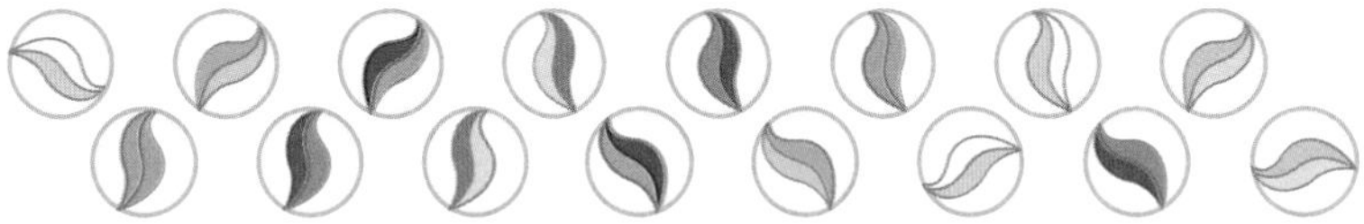 Half of 16 is [ ]

g. 12 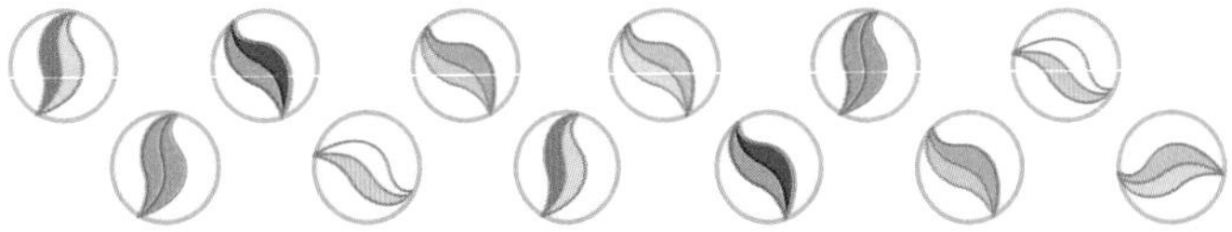 Half of 12 is [ ]

h. 20 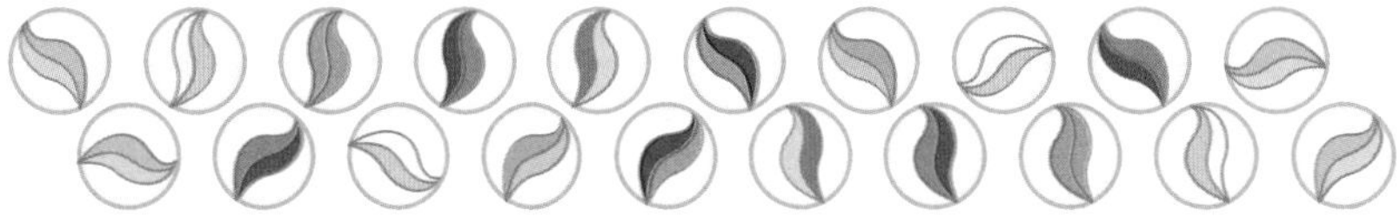 Half of 20 is [ ]

2 Tammy wants to give Nikki and Rihana equal numbers of sweets. How many sweets will each friend get?

a. 
2 each

b. 
each

c. 
each

d. 
each

e. 
each

f. 
each

3 Fill half the boxes with chocolates.

a. 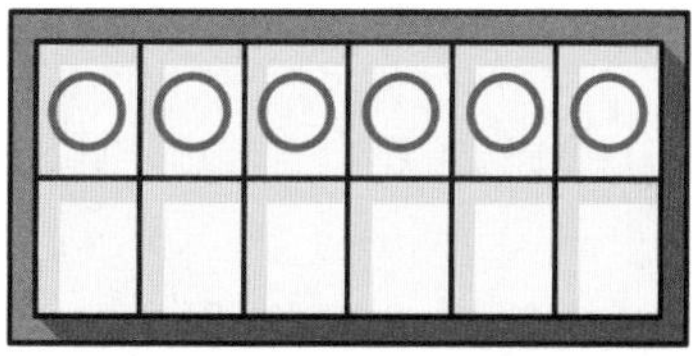

b. 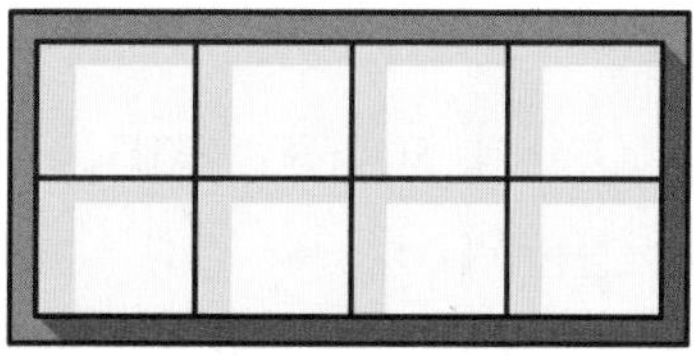

c. 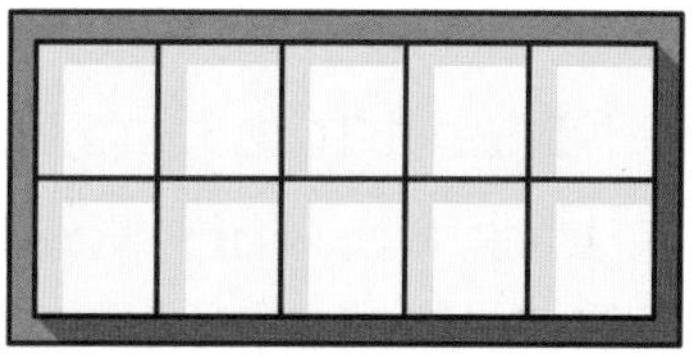

d. 

e. 

◆ I can divide a group of objects into halves. ☐

Let's try this!

You need these number cards:
2, 4, 6, 8, 10, 12, 14, 16, 18, 20.
Mix up the cards.
Lay them face down on the table.
Pick up a card.
Halve the number.

4.3 Quarters of shapes

- I can understand quarters.

Key words
fraction, quarter, divide, same, equal

A **quarter** is a fraction. It means something has been divided into **four** parts. The four parts must be the **same size** to be quarters.

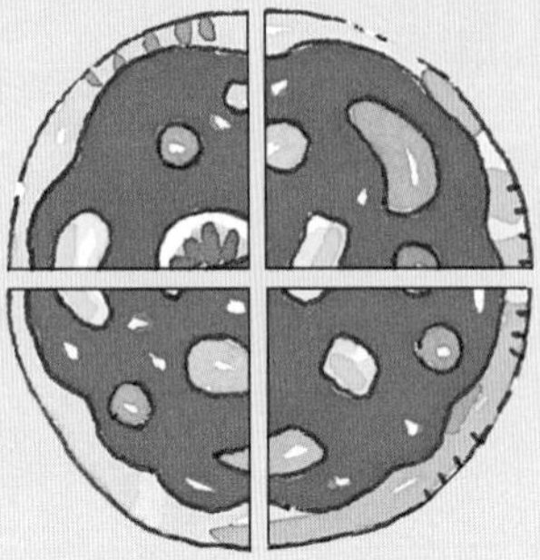
Quarters

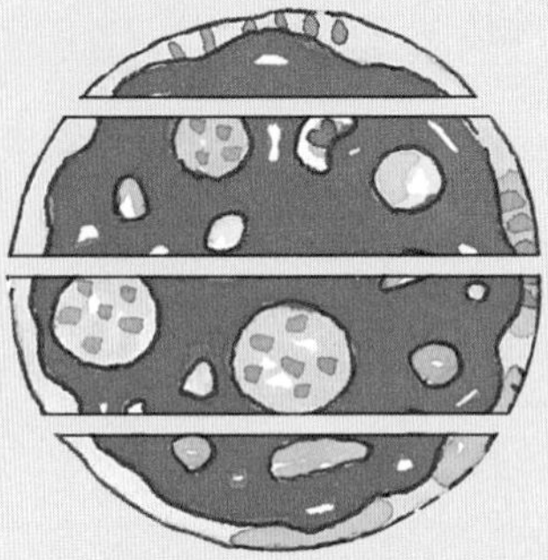
Not quarters

1 Meena has been trying to cut some things into quarters.
Tick the ones which are quarters.
Remember, to be quarters the four parts must be **equal**.

a.  ✗

b. 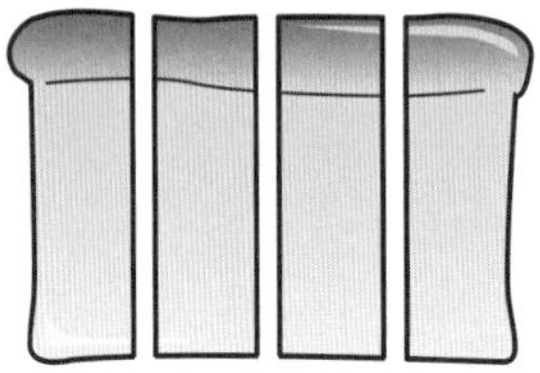

c. 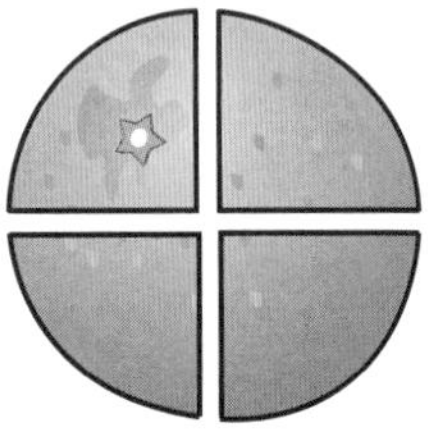

d. 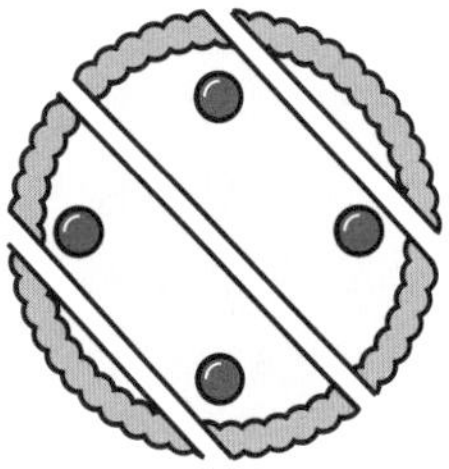

e. 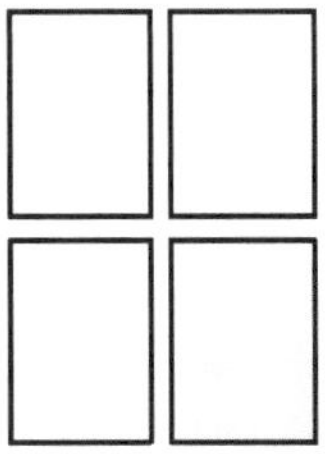

f. 

g. 

h. 

i. 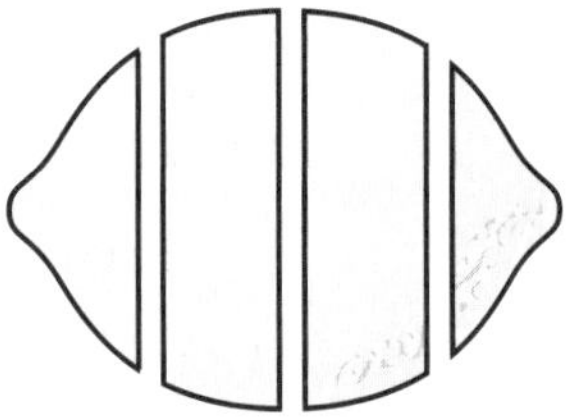

2 Draw lines to cut these objects into quarters.

a.

b.

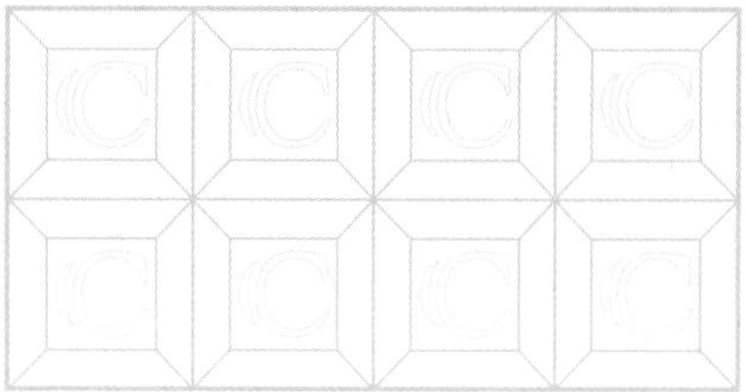

c.

d.

e.

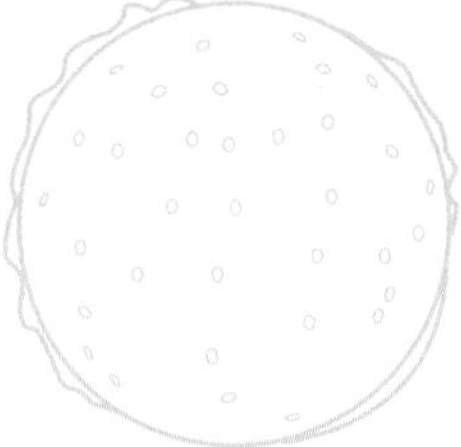

f.

g.

h.

i.

j.

I can divide an object into quarters. ☐

Let's try this!

Choose five things.
Draw them.
Draw lines to cut them into quarters.

4.4 Quarters of numbers

- I can share a group of objects into quarters.

Key words
fraction, quarter, share, equal

Groups of things can be put into quarters.
It is like sharing between four people.
The groups must all be **equal** to be quarters.
Get four pots and 12 marbles.
Put a quarter of the marbles into each pot.

1 You will need some marbles and four pots.
Share the marbles between the four pots.

a. 8 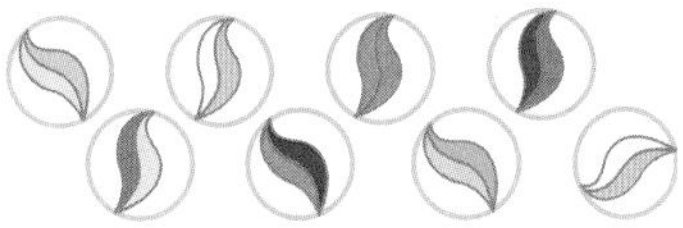 Quarter of 8 is [2]

b. 4 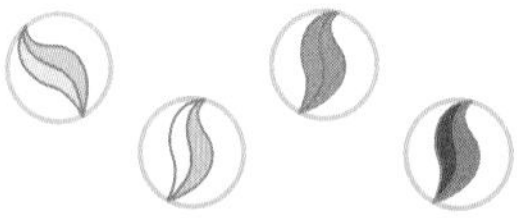 Quarter of 4 is [ ]

c. 16 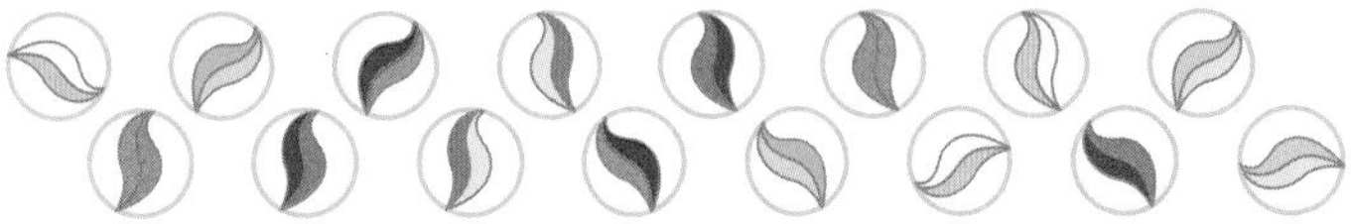 Quarter of 16 is [ ]

d. 20 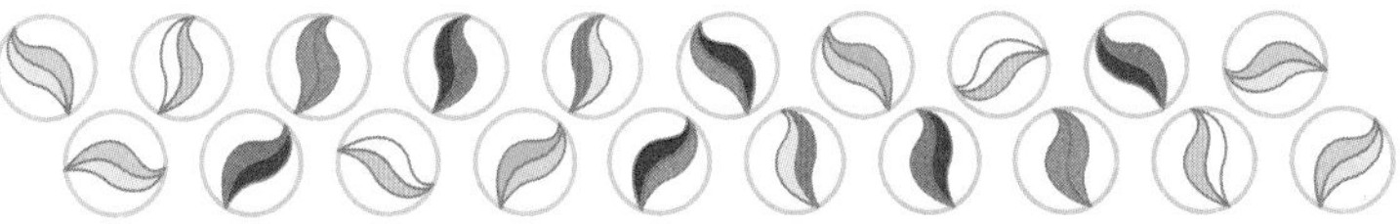 Quarter of 20 is [ ]

e. 12 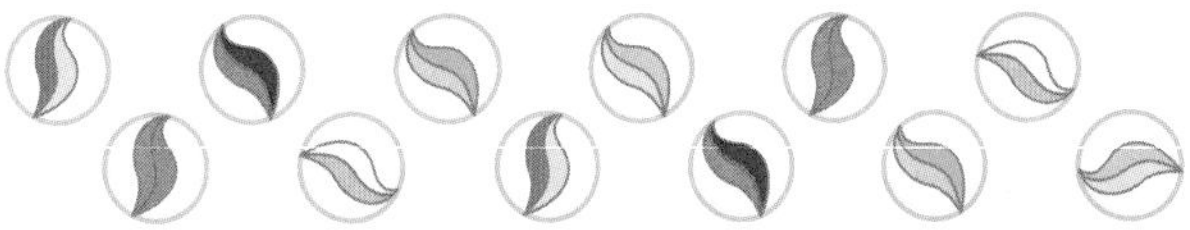 Quarter of 12 is [ ]

f. 24 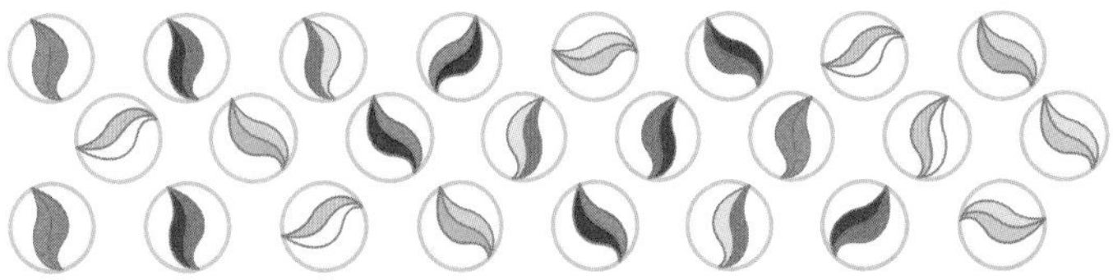 Quarter of 24 is [ ]

2 Otunga wants to give four of his friends equal numbers of sweets. How many sweets will each friend get?

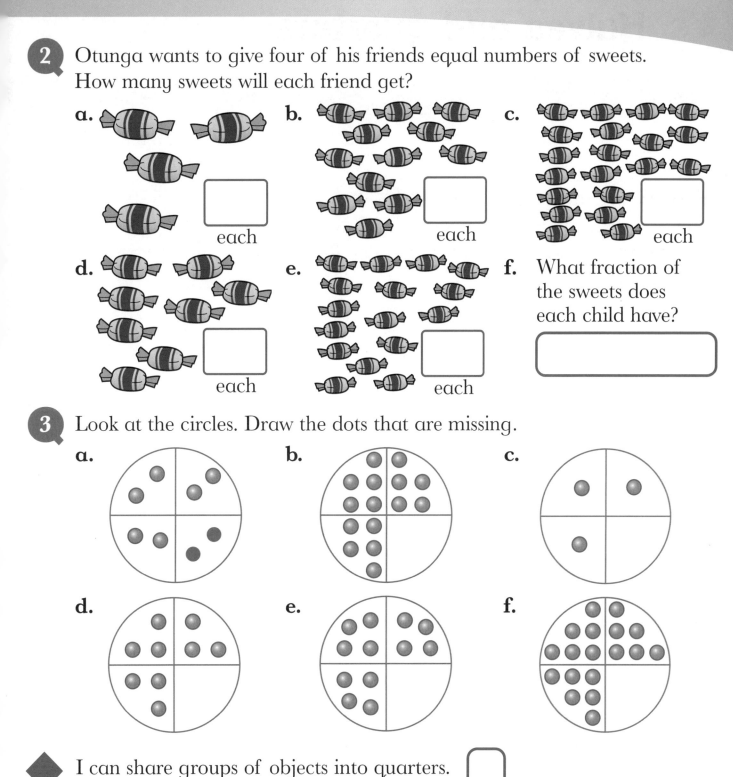

a.

each

b.

each

c.
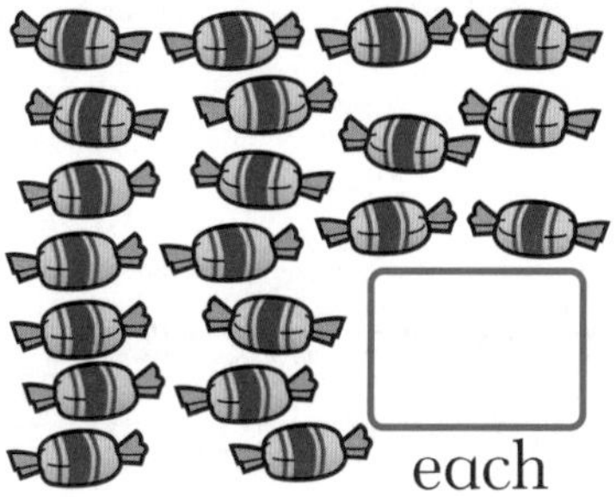
each

d.

each

e.

each

f. What fraction of the sweets does each child have?

3 Look at the circles. Draw the dots that are missing.

a.
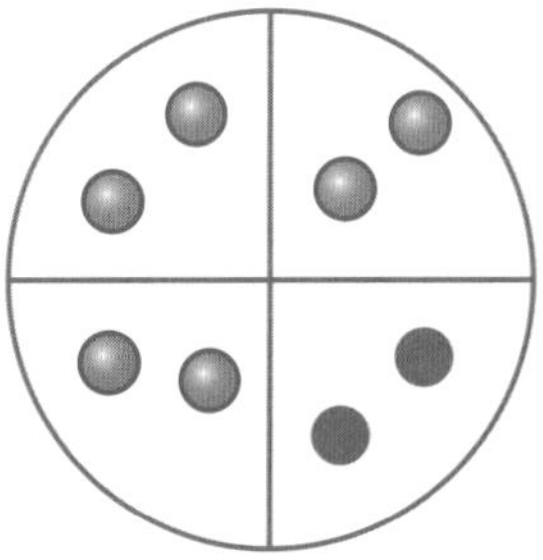

b.
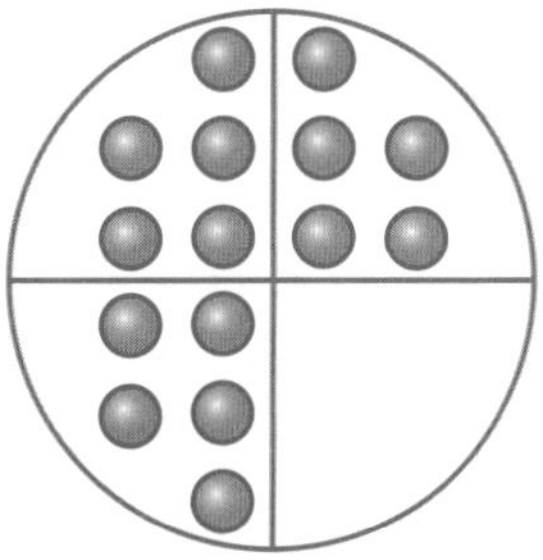

c.
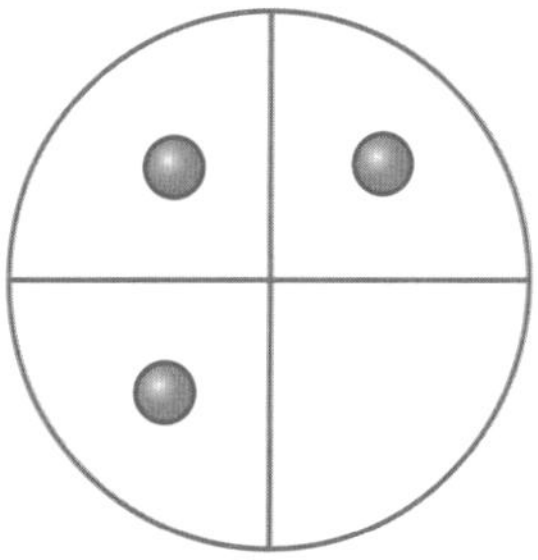

d.
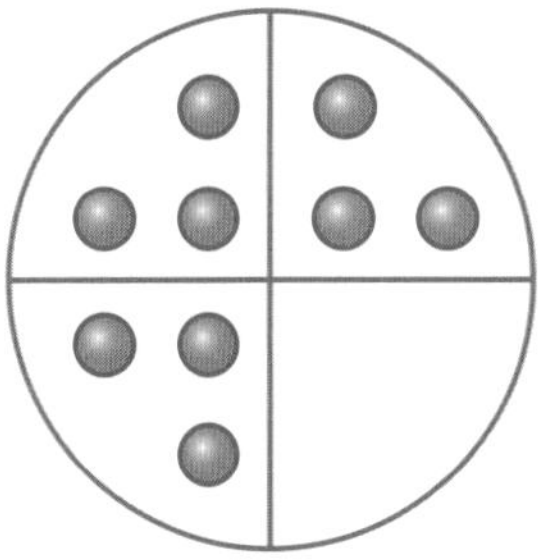

e.
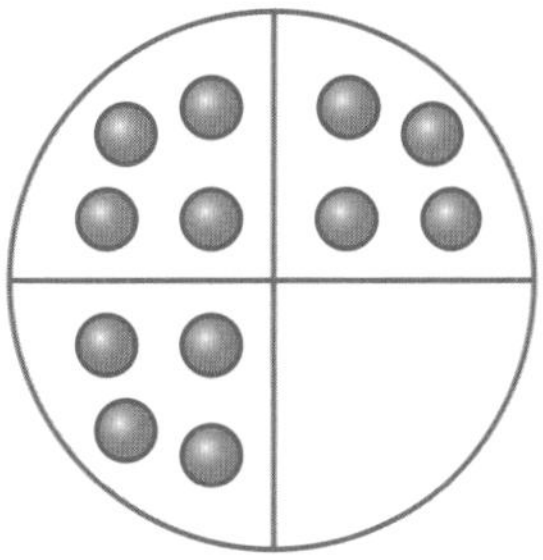

f.
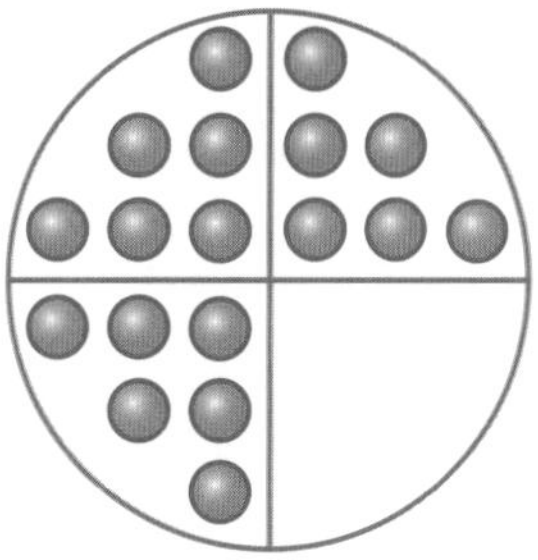

I can share groups of objects into quarters.

Let's try this!

Get a handful of marbles. Draw four circles on a piece of paper. Share the marbles into quarters. Do they share equally? Write down the numbers that make quarters and the numbers that do not.

4.5 Halves and quarters

- I can understand halves and quarters.

Key words
half, divide, quarter, fraction

Halves and **quarters** are both fractions.
Halves mean you divide something into two parts.
Quarters mean you divide something into four parts.

Half can be written like this $\frac{1}{2}$.

Quarter can be written like this $\frac{1}{4}$.

The number at the bottom tells you how many parts to divide into.

1 Look at the shapes.
What fraction is coloured? Write $\frac{1}{2}$ or $\frac{1}{4}$ next to the shape.

a. 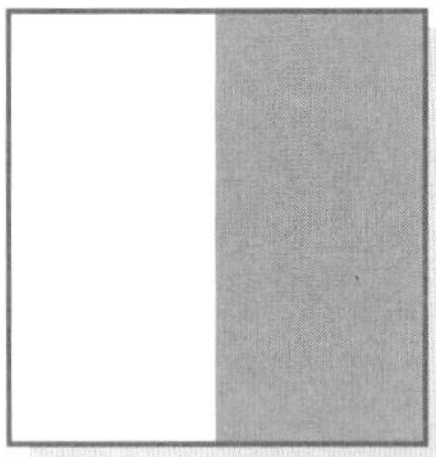 $\frac{1}{2}$

b. 

c. 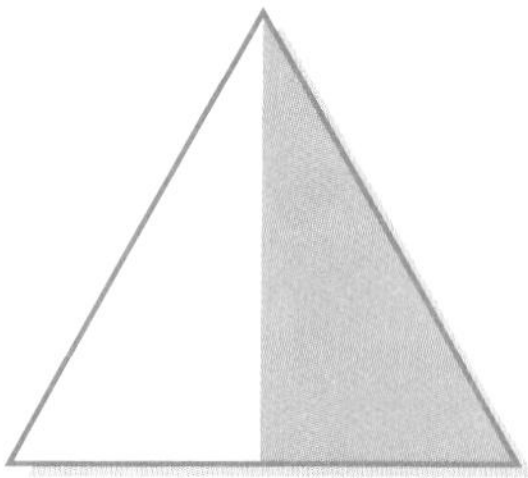

d. 

e. 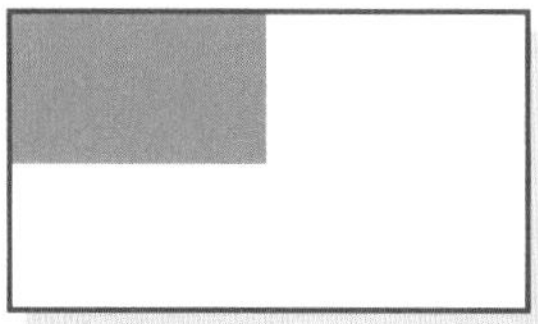

f.  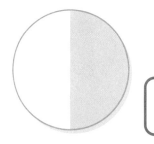 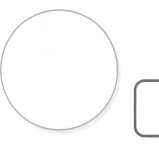 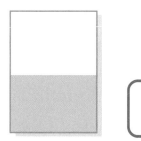

g. 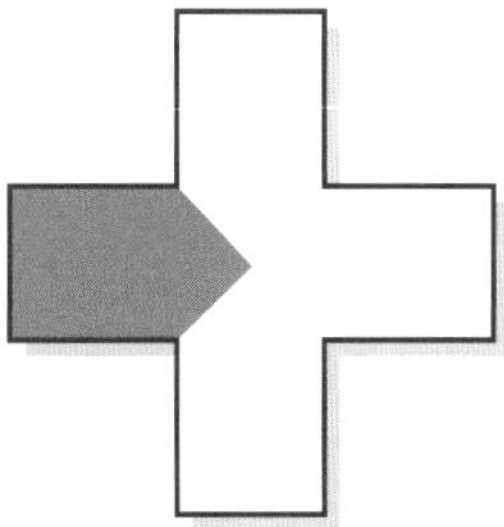

h. 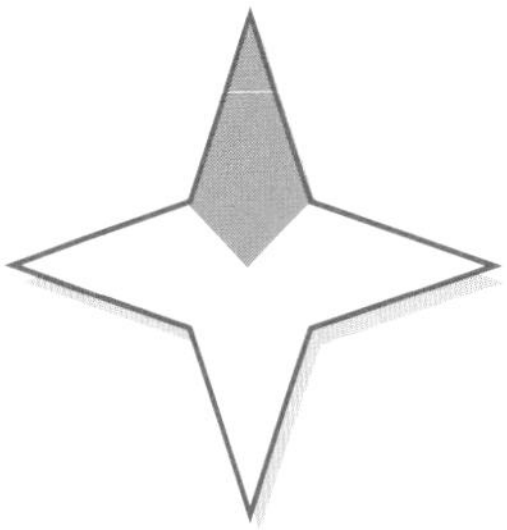

i. 

2 Draw around half of these pizzas.

a.

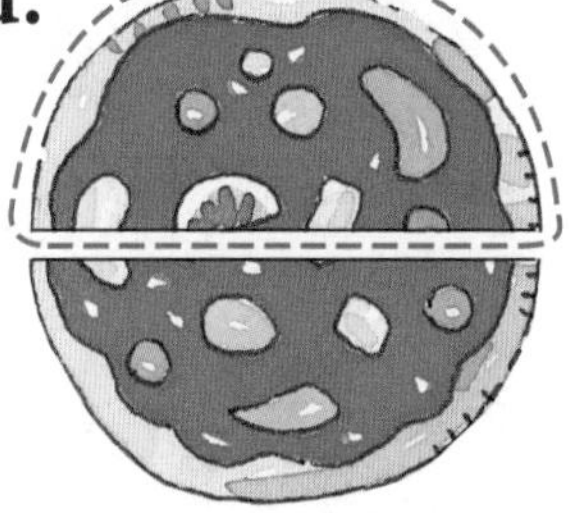

b.

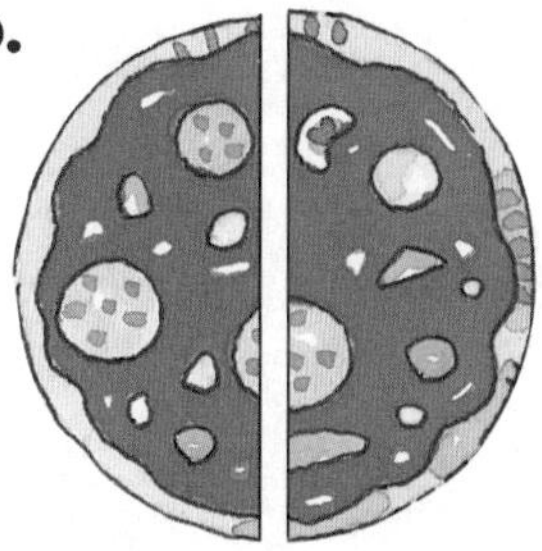

c.

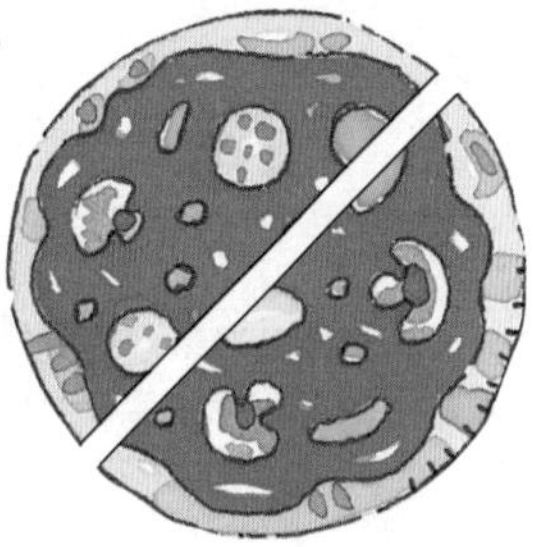

d.

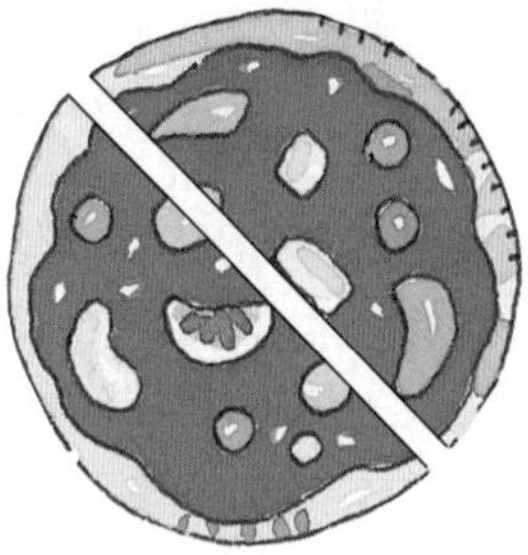

3 Draw around a quarter of these pizzas.

a.

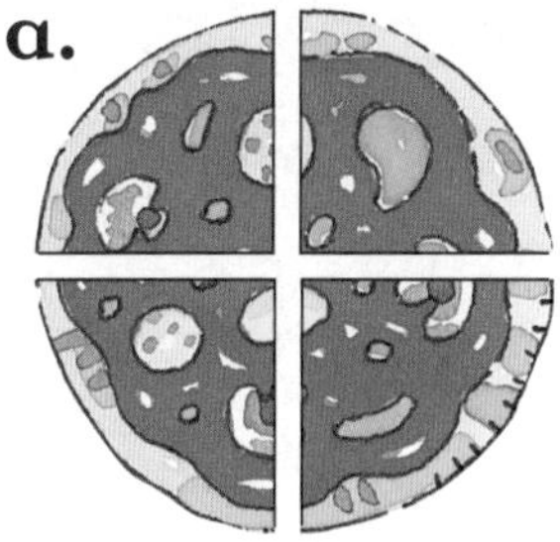

b.

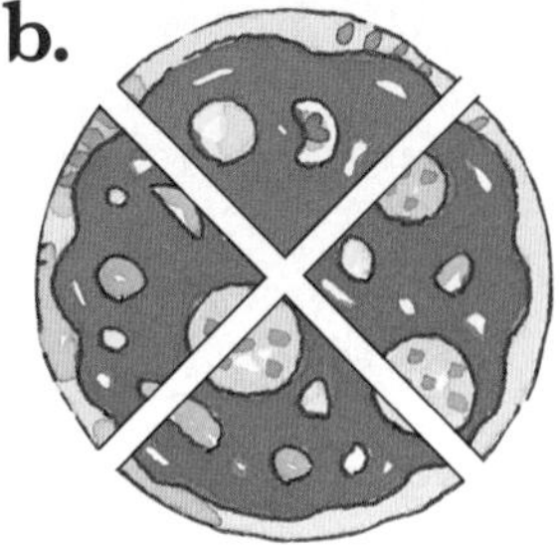

4 Look at the pictures of containers. Colour each one so it is half full.

a.

b.

c.

d.

e.

f.

◆ I can use halves and quarters. ☐

Let's try this!

Four friends have six apples.
How can they have a quarter each?
Draw your answer.

MEASURE – LENGTH AND TIME

5.1 Measuring in metres

- I can estimate and measure lengths in metres and in half metres.

Key words
metre (m), half metre ($\frac{1}{2}$ m), estimate, measure, length, width, about

Let's play a game.

You will need a metre measuring stick, a strip of ribbon, a marker and an empty tin.

Use the measuring stick to mark 1, 2 and 3 metres on the ribbon.

Cut off any extra bit. This is your measuring tape!

Roll the tin along the floor.

How far did it roll?

Measure this with your tape.

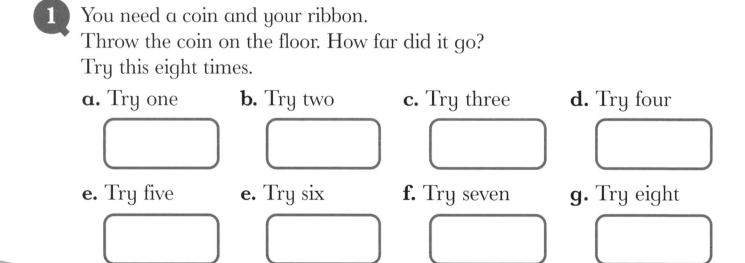

1 You need a coin and your ribbon.
Throw the coin on the floor. How far did it go?
Try this eight times.

a. Try one **b.** Try two **c.** Try three **d.** Try four

e. Try five **e.** Try six **f.** Try seven **g.** Try eight

2 Get your 3 m ribbon and fold it in half.
Mark the fold line with a pen. This measures $1\frac{1}{2}$ m.

The red line measures $1\frac{1}{2}$ m.

Now fold the 1 m part in half and mark the fold line with a pen. This measures $\frac{1}{2}$ m. Measure some things in your classroom. Estimate their lengths and measure them.

Things to measure	Estimate	Measure
Length of table	about 2 m	$2\frac{1}{2}$ m
Length of		

3 Write the length shown by the arrow.

a.

Length = 7 m

b.

Length = ☐ m

c.

Length = ☐ m

d.

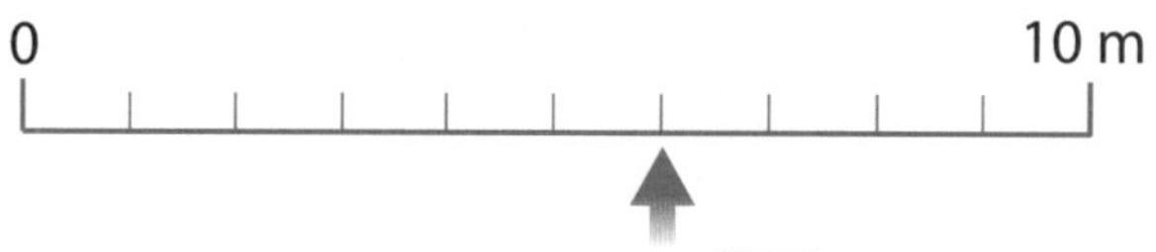

Length = ☐ m

I can estimate and measure lengths in m and in $\frac{1}{2}$ m. ☐

Let's try this!

Use your 3 m ribbon to find the length and width of your classroom, the corridor and the entrance hall.

5.2 Measuring in centimetres

- I can estimate and measure lengths in centimetres.

Key words
estimate, measure, centimetre (cm), length, longer than, longest, shorter than, shortest

1 **a.** Estimate then measure the length of each ribbon in centimetres. Write down your answers.

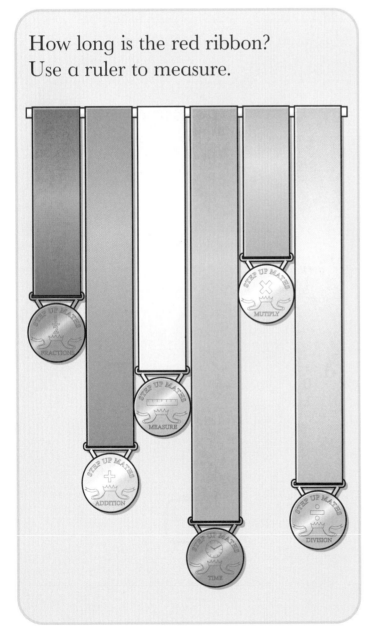

How long is the red ribbon?
Use a ruler to measure.

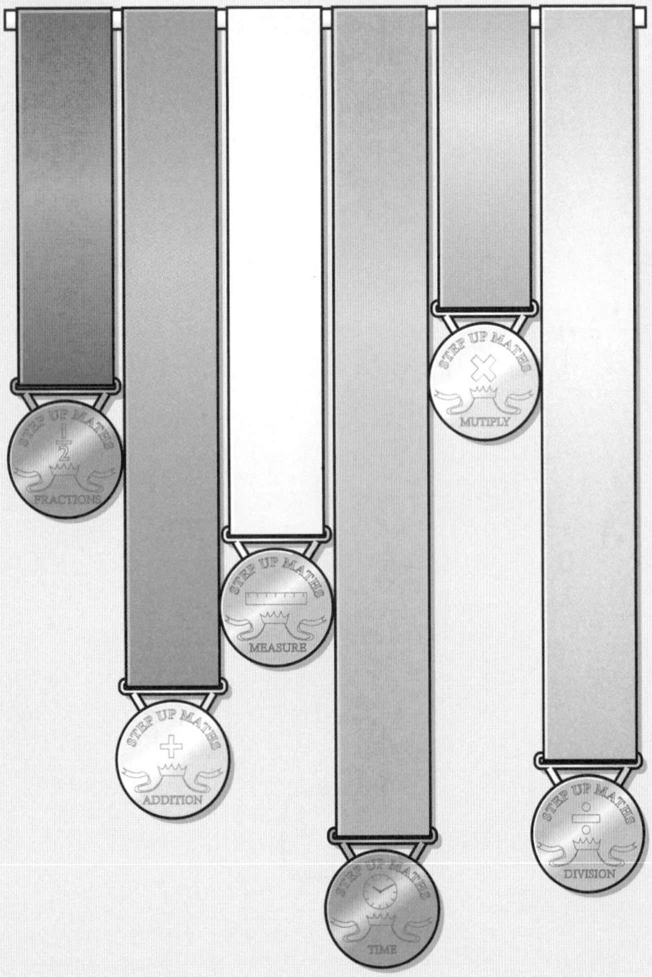

Colour	Estimate	Measure
Red	6 cm	5 cm
Green		
Yellow		
Orange		
Pink		
Blue		

b. The shortest ribbon is ☐ cm long.

c. The longest ribbon is ☐ cm long.

d. The yellow ribbon is ☐ cm shorter than the blue ribbon.

e. The ☐ ribbon is 7 cm longer than the ☐ ribbon.

2

Use a ruler to measure the length of each green line in centimetres.

Green line	a	b	c	d	e
Length in cm	4 cm				

3 Draw a line that is:

a. 5 cm **longer** than Jet a

4 cm + 5 cm = 9 cm

b. 4 cm **longer** than Jet b

c. 3 cm **longer** than Jet d

d. 4 cm **shorter** than Jet c

e. 5 cm **shorter** than Jet e

I can estimate and measure lengths in cm. ☐

Let's try this!

Find five small things. Measure them in centimetres.
Make a straight line with your five things and find their total length.

5.3 How long is it?

- I can compare lengths and measure a length in centimetres.

Key words
compare, measure, centimetre (cm), length, order, shorter, longer, between

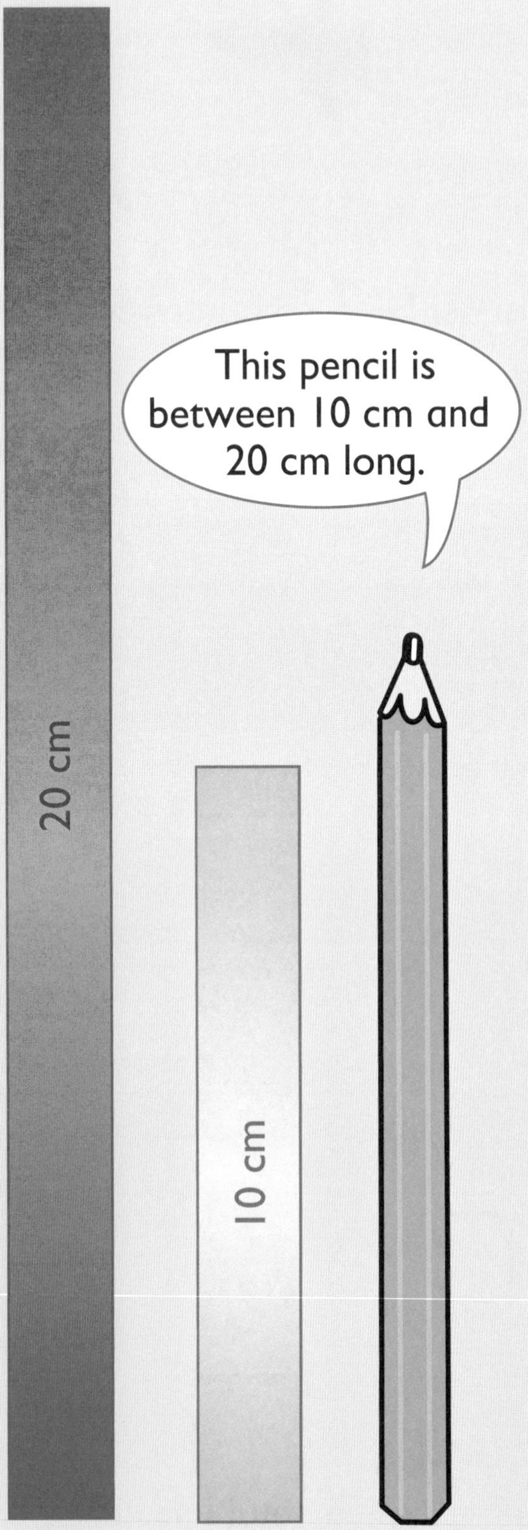

This pencil is between 10 cm and 20 cm long.
20 cm
10 cm

1 Find any 10 things, such as a pencil, book, eraser, your hand etc.
Put each thing with the red and blue strips.
Write their names in the correct boxes.

10 cm or shorter	Between 10 cm and 20 cm	Longer than 20 cm
	pencil	

Now, count the items in each box and complete the sentences.

☐ things are shorter than 10 cm.

☐ things are between 10 cm and 20 cm.

☐ things are longer than 20 cm.

2 Join all the dots in order.

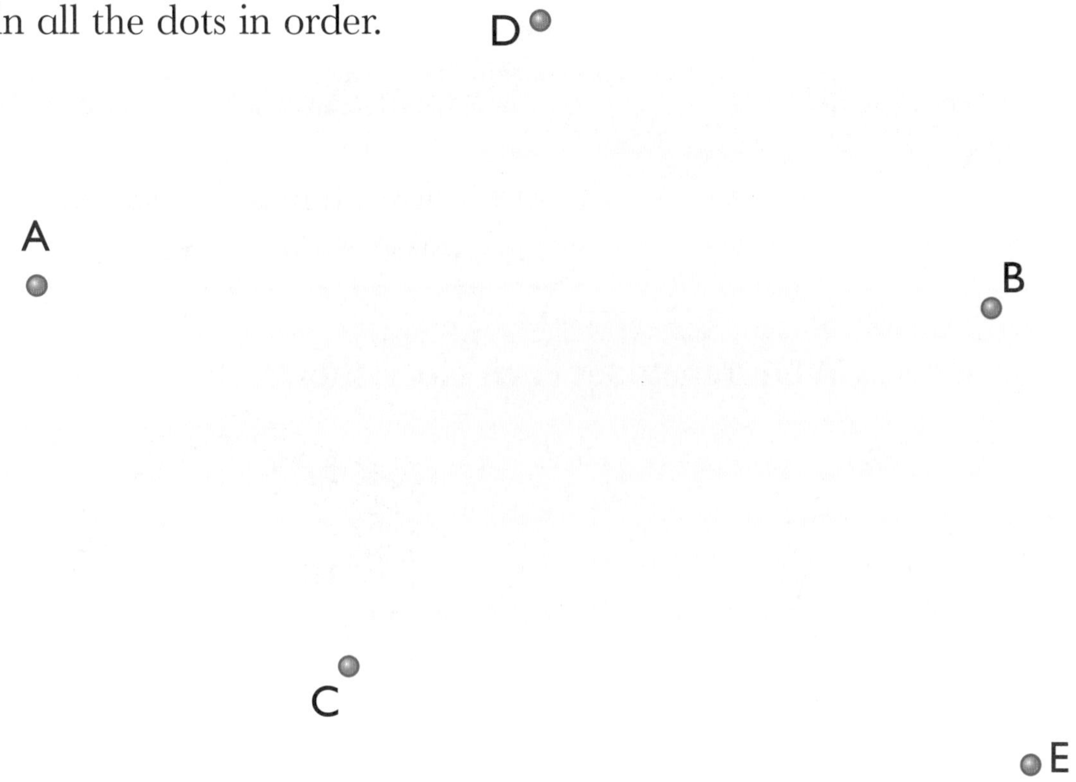

Measure how long it is:

a. from A to B [13] cm **b.** from C to D [ ] cm

c. from D to E [ ] cm **d.** from E to A [ ] cm

e. from C to B [ ] cm

f. Write the lengths of the lines in order. Begin with the shortest line.

....

g. What shape do the lines make? ....

◆ I can compare lengths and measure a length in cm. ☐

Let's try this!

Get a sheet of paper and a ruler.
Draw a very large letter Z.
Find a way to measure the total length of your letter Z.

5.4 Time clocks

- I can tell the time to the hour and $\frac{1}{2}$ hour on a clock face.

Key words
time, clock, hours, $\frac{1}{2}$ past, half past, ago, later, minutes (min)

What time does each clock show?

You can write the time each clock shows like this:

1 o'clock
Minute hand is at 12.
Hour hand is at 1.

$\frac{1}{2}$ past 1 or half past one
Minute hand is at 6.
Hour hand is halfway between 1 and 2.

1 Look at these clocks. Write the time each clock shows.

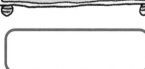

a.

b.

c.

d.

2 Draw hands to show these times.

a. 7 o'clock

b. 9 o'clock

c. 6 o'clock

d. $\frac{1}{2}$ past 8

e. $\frac{1}{2}$ past 2

f. $\frac{1}{2}$ past 12

3 Write the time this clock showed:

a. 2 hours ago.

b. half an hour ago.

c. 2 hours later.

d. half an hour later.

◆ I can tell the time to the hour and half hour on a clock face. ☐

Let's try this!

Kenny saw this clock in a mirror.
What time did it show?

5.5 Digital times

- I can tell the time to the hour and $\frac{1}{2}$ hour on a digital clock.

Key words
time, digital, hours (h), half past

Look at these digital clocks.
Match the answers to the clocks.

1 o'clock 2 o'clock $\frac{1}{2}$ past 2

1:00 1:30 2:00 2:30

$\frac{1}{2}$ past 1 one thirty two thirty

Remember, you can write the $\frac{1}{2}$ past times in two ways.

1 Write the time each digital clock shows.

a. 9:00 — 9 o'clock

b. 4:00

c. 12:00

d. 2:30

e. 11:30

f. 8:30

g. 5:00

h. 6:30

i. 7:30

2 This is Jordan's digital watch.
Write the digital time it showed:

a. 2 hours ago. [:]

b. $\frac{1}{2}$ an hour ago. [:]

c. 2 hours later. [:]

d. $\frac{1}{2}$ an hour later. [:]

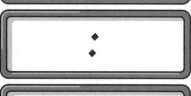

3 The check-in times are 2 hours before the take-off times.
Write the check-in times on each case.

	TAKE-OFF TIME
Florida	6 o'clock
Spain	half past 9
Italy	1 o'clock
Greece	half past 12

◆ I can tell the time to the hour and half-hour on a digital clock. ☐

Let's try this!

Alison said, 'I can make more than five different hour and half hour digital times with these cards.'
Find out if she is right.

Understanding Shapes

6.1 Common 2-D shapes

- I can name and describe 2-D shapes.

Key words
circle, triangle, square, rectangle, pentagon, hexagon, side, straight, curved

Triangle
It has three sides. Its sides are straight.

Circle
It has one side. Its side is curved.

Pentagon
It has five sides. Its sides are straight.

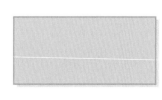

Rectangle
It has four sides. Its sides are straight.

Square
It has four sides. Its sides are straight.

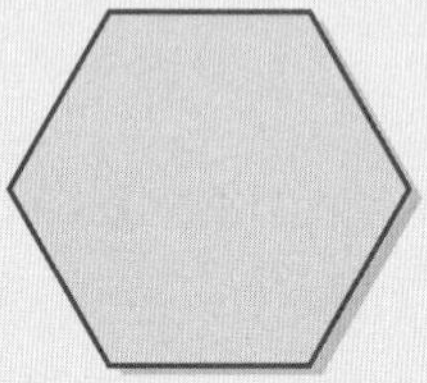

Hexagon
It has six sides. Its sides are straight.

1 Write the names of these shapes in the boxes.

a.

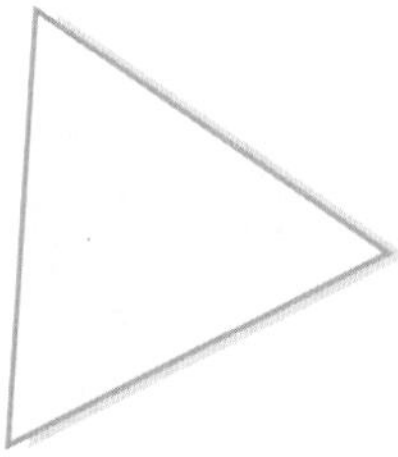

Triangle

b.

c.

d.

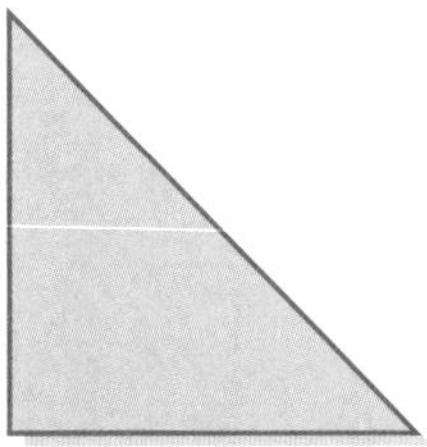

e.

f.

2 Draw the shapes in the boxes.

Curved sides only	**Straight sides only**
Less than four sides	**Four sides**

3 Colour the shapes with:

- three sides in **blue**.
- four sides in **red**.
- curved sides only in **yellow**.
- straight and curved sides in **green**.

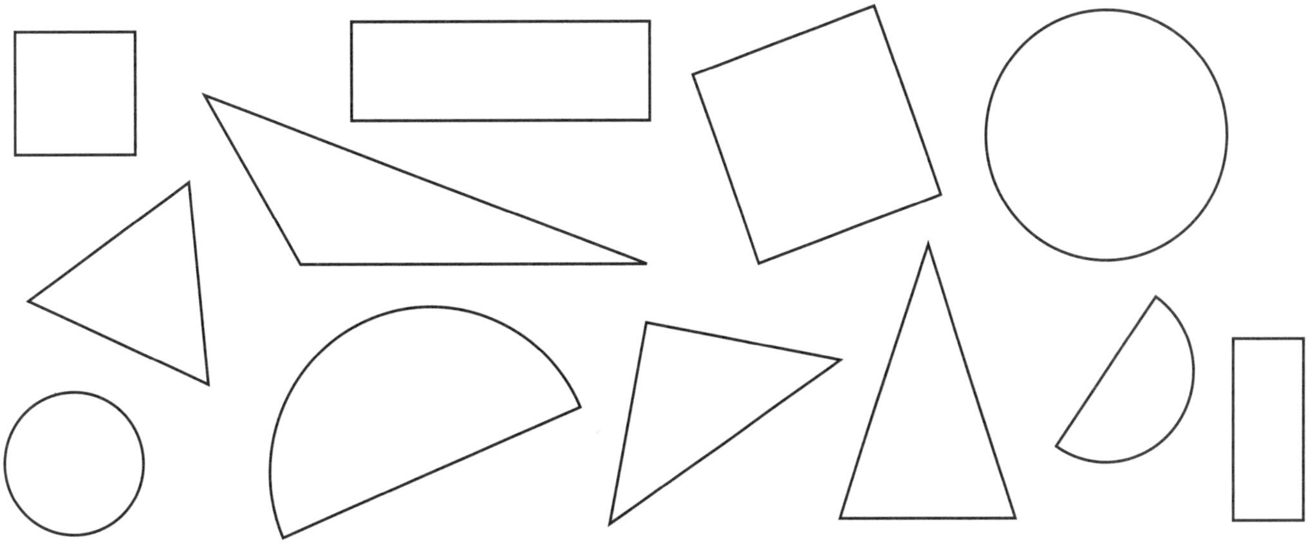

I can name and describe 2-D shapes. ☐

Let's try this!

Look at these shapes.
How are they:

a. alike?
b. different?

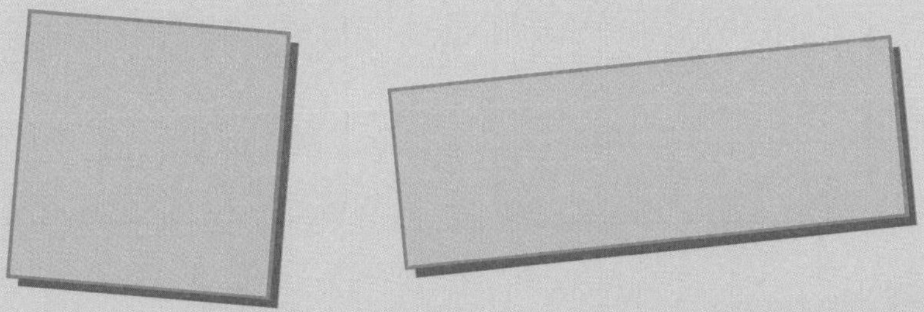

6.2 Pinboard shapes

- I can make 2-D shapes using a pinboard.

Key words
circle, triangle, square, rectangle, side, 5 sided, 6 sided, pinboard

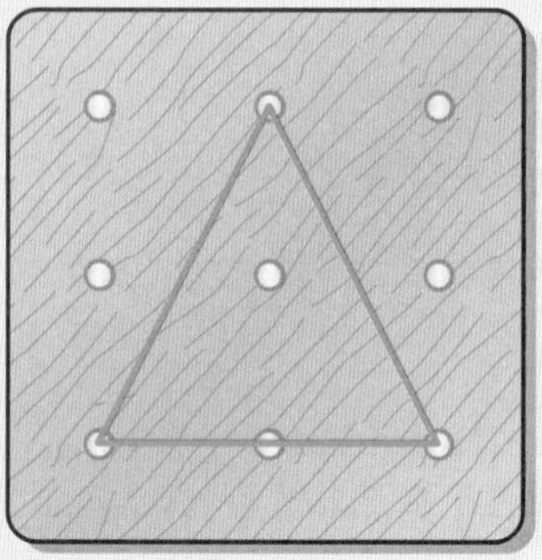

I can make a triangle on a pinboard with a rubber band.

1 You will need a rubber band and a 3 × 3 pinboard.
Make shapes on your pinboard with the rubber band.
Draw the shapes you make.

a. Two different triangles

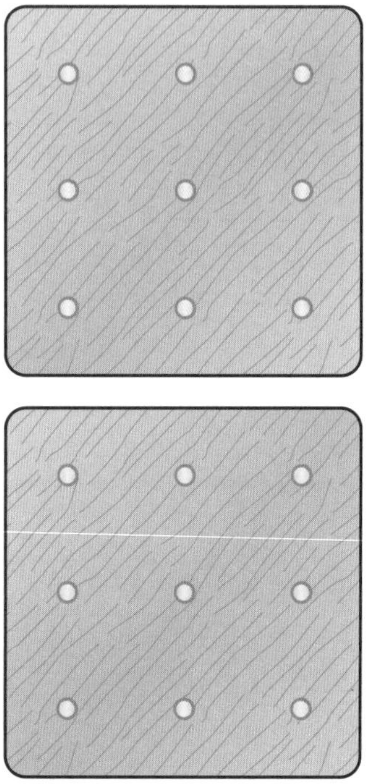

b. Two different squares

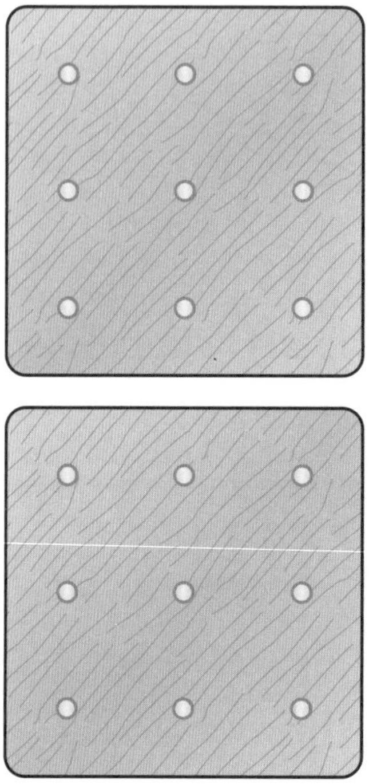

c. Two different rectangles

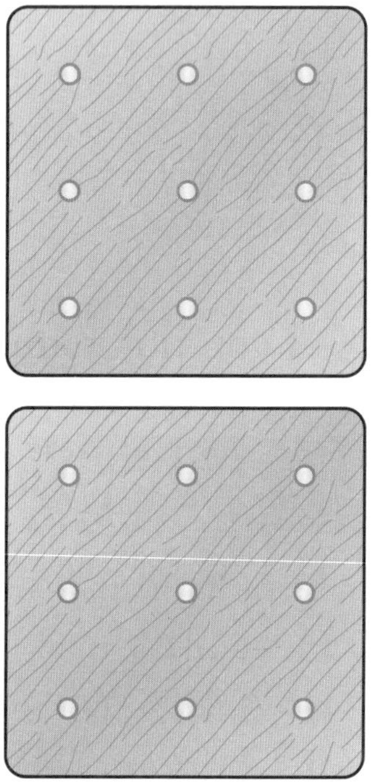

2 Make these shapes on your pinboard.

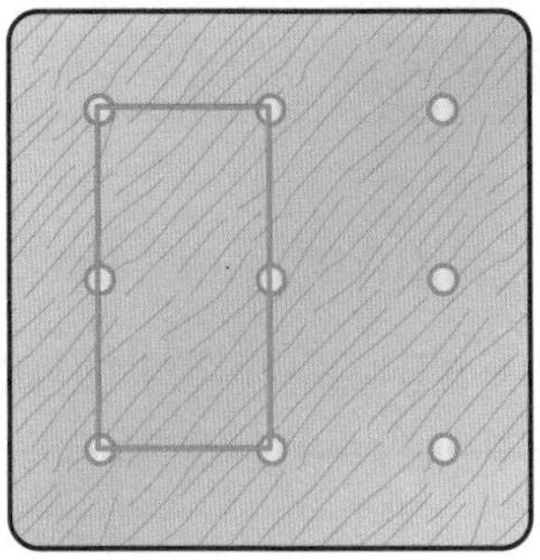
4 sides

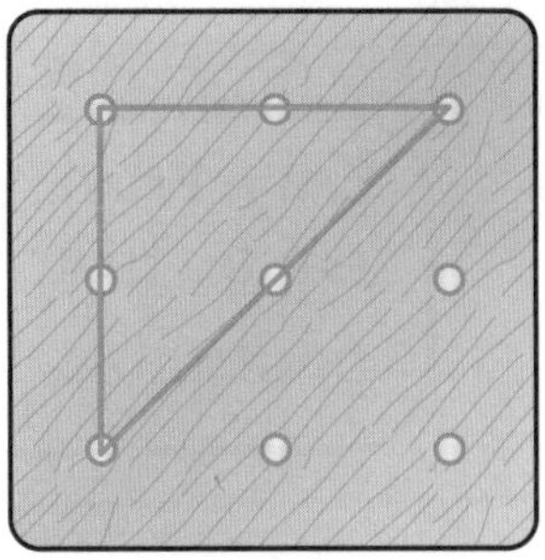
3 sides

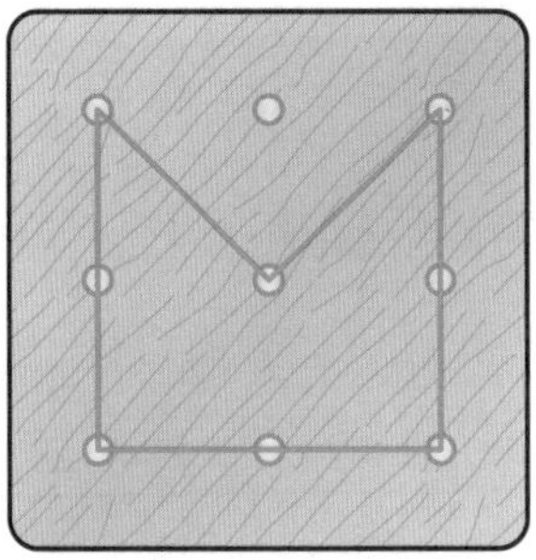
5 sides

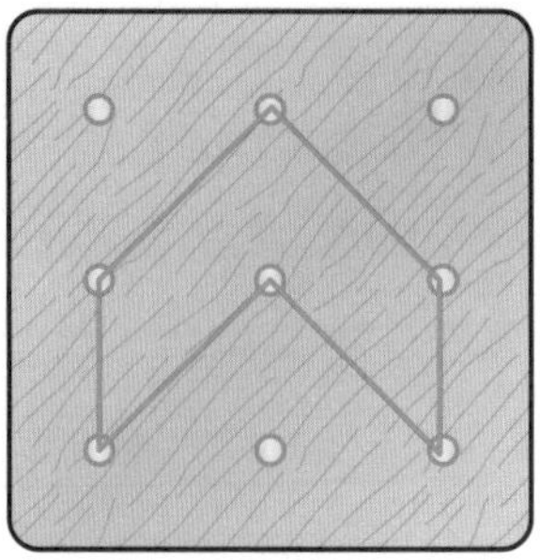
6 sides

3 Count the number of sides for each shape.

a.

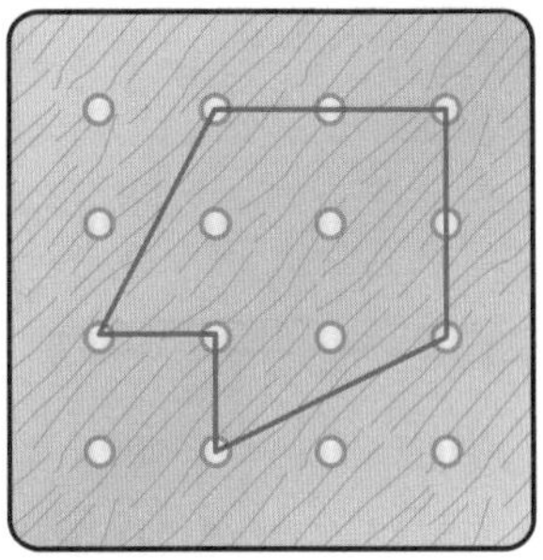
☐ sides

b.

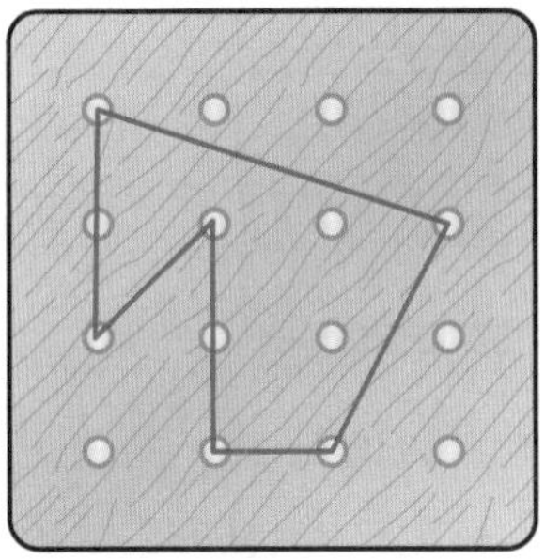
☐ sides

c.

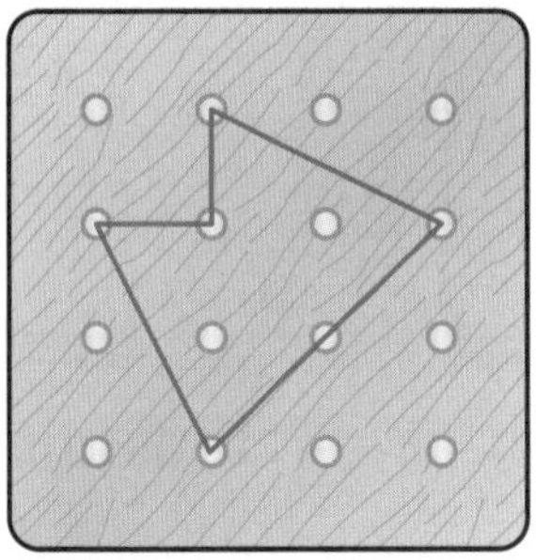
☐ sides

d.

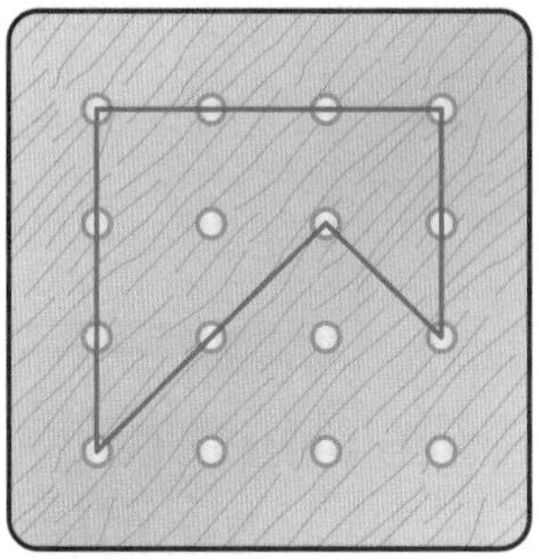
☐ sides

e.

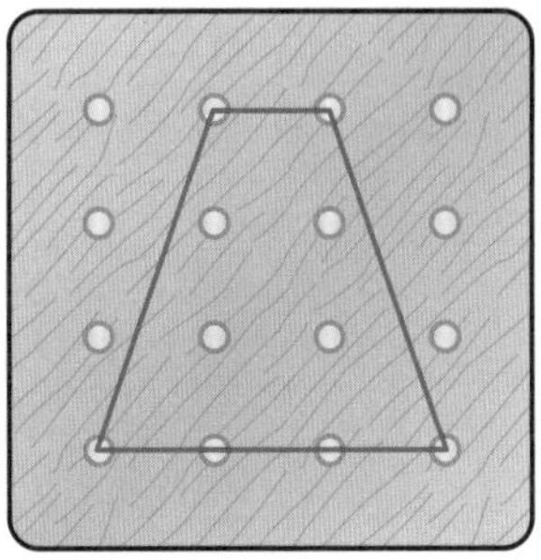
☐ sides

f.

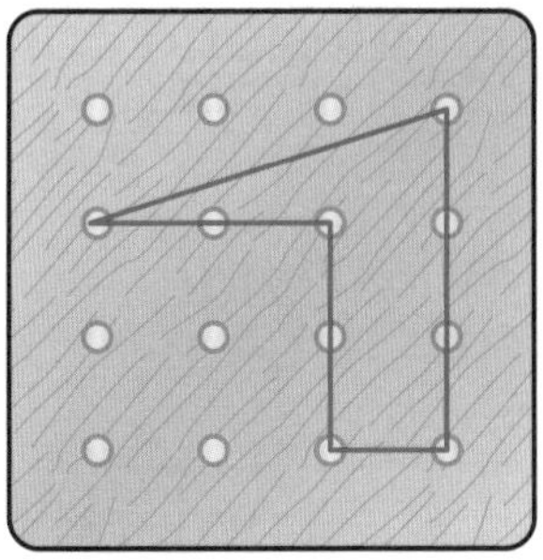
☐ sides

g.

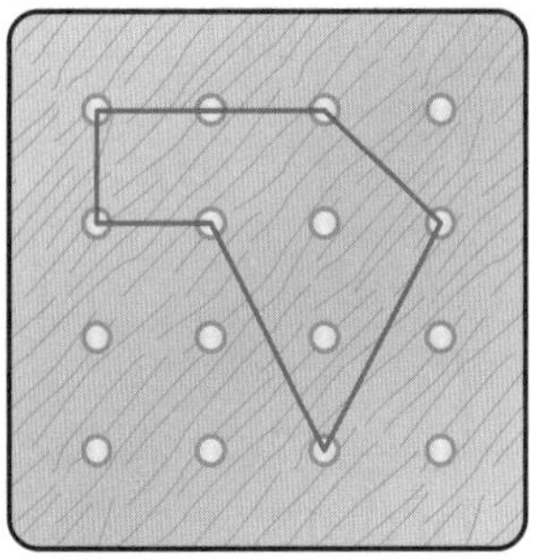
☐ sides

h.

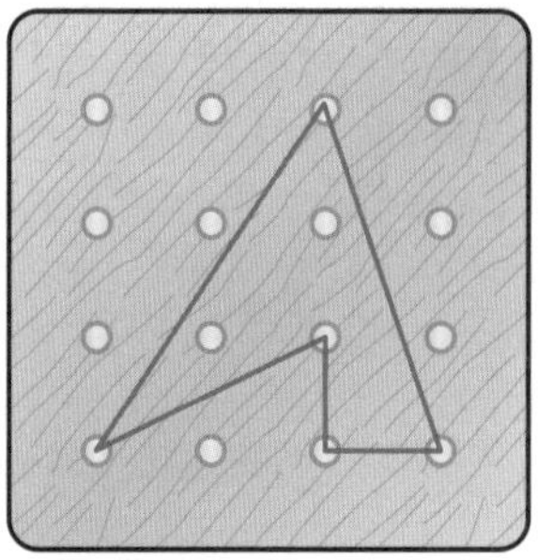
☐ sides

◆ I can make 2-D shapes using a pinboard. ☐

Let's try this!

Get five straws, some short and some long.
How many five sided shapes can you make?

6.3 Sides and corners

- I can count the number of sides and corners and name the shape.

Key words
circle, triangle, square, rectangle, pentagon, hexagon, corner, side

What shapes do I make when I cut a slice of bread in half?

This slice of bread is a rectangle.
A rectangle has 4 sides and 4 corners.

This slice of bread is cut into two rectangles.
Each rectangle has 4 sides and 4 corners.

This slice of bread is cut into two triangles.
Each triangle has 3 sides and 3 corners.

1 For each shape count the number of sides and corners and write its name.

a.

☐ sides
☐ corners

☐

b.

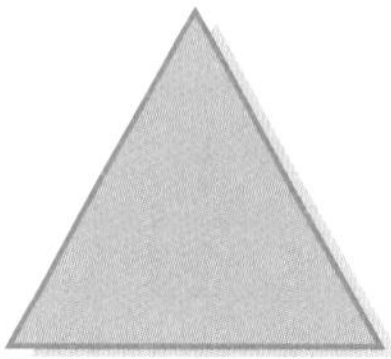

☐ sides
☐ corners

☐

c.

☐ sides
☐ corners

☐

d.

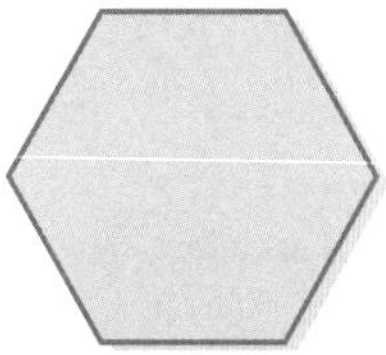

☐ sides
☐ corners

☐

e.

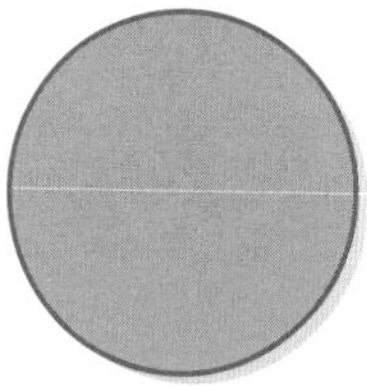

☐ sides
☐ corners

☐

f.

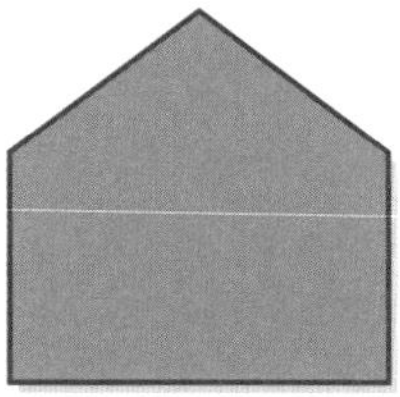

☐ sides
☐ corners

☐

g. 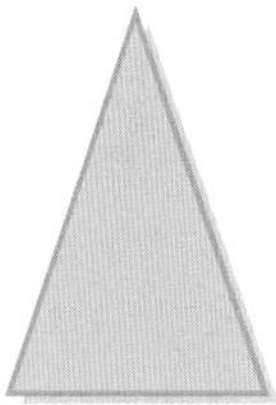

☐ sides ☐ corners

☐

h. 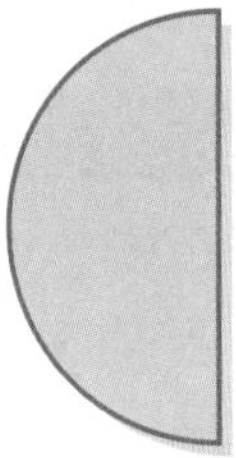

☐ sides ☐ corners

☐

i. 

☐ sides ☐ corners

☐

j. 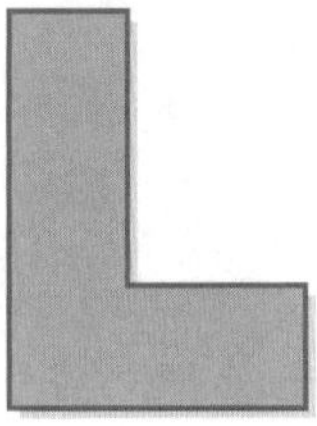

☐ sides ☐ corners

☐

2 Each of these shapes is made with four squares.
Write the number of corners in each shape.

a. 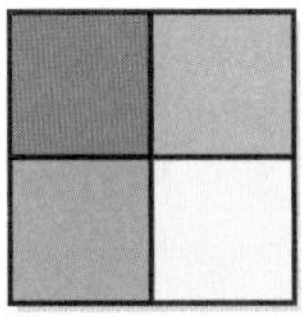

☐ corners

b. 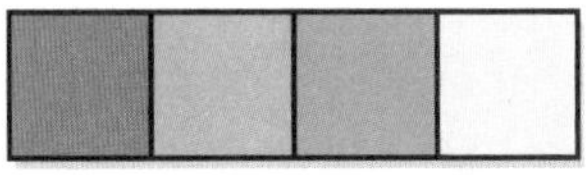

☐ corners

c. 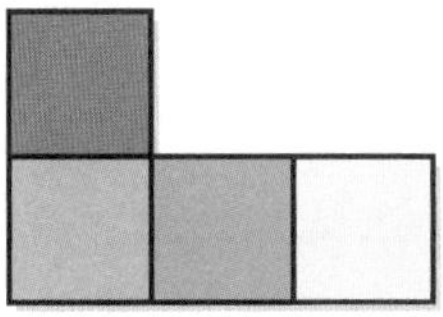

☐ corners

d. 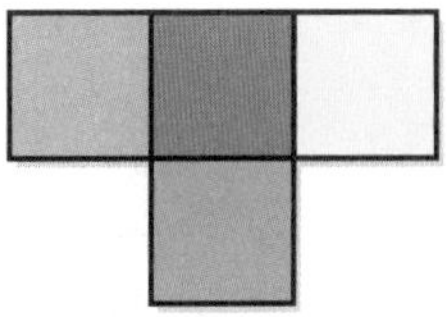

☐ corners

e. 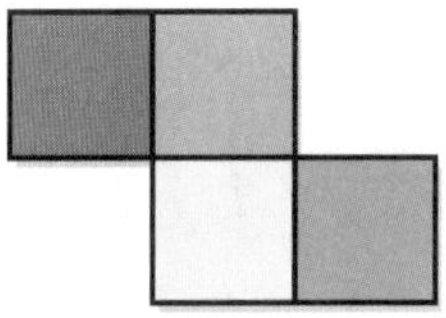

☐ corners

f. 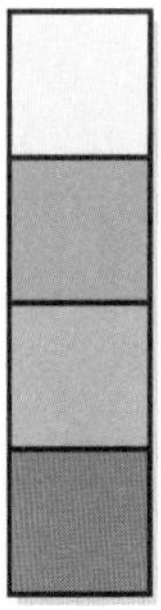

☐ corners

◆ I can count the number of sides and corners and name the shape. ☐

Let's try this!

Get five square cards.
Make five shapes with them.
Draw your five shapes.
How many corners do they have?

This shape has **8** corners.

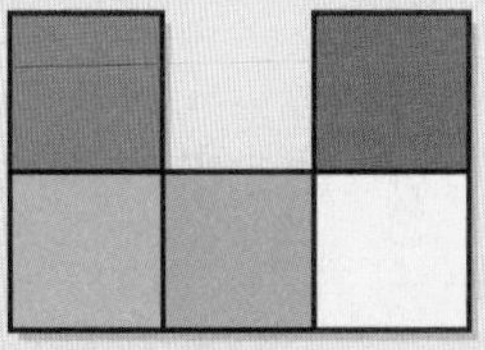

6.4 Common 3-D solids

- I can match 3-D solids to their pictures and describe them.

Key words
cone, cube, cuboid, cylinder, sphere, face, corner, flat, curved, rectangular, solid

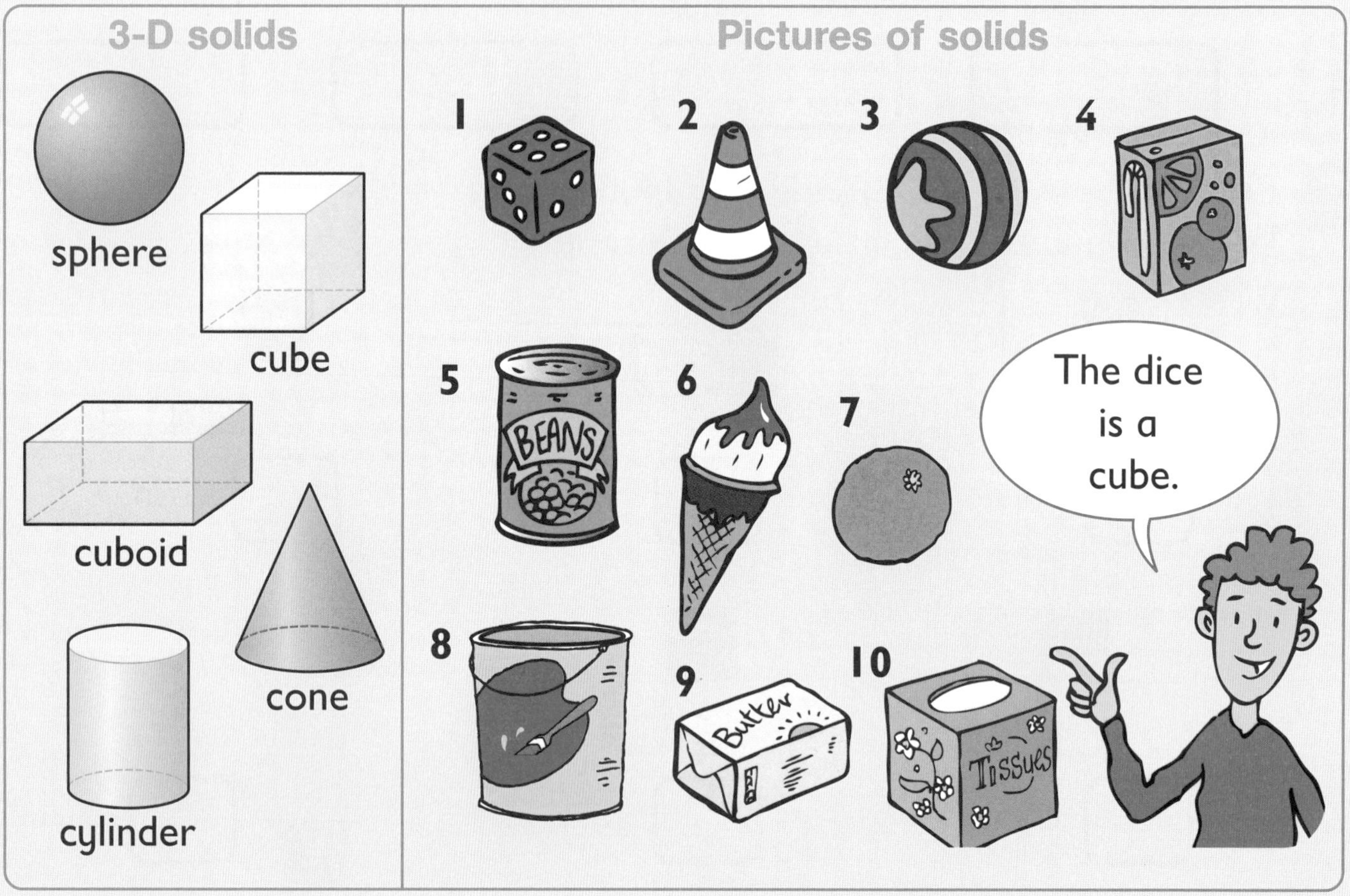

1 Match each picture to its solid.

Picture	Solid
1	cube
2	
3	
4	
5	

Picture	Solid
6	
7	
8	
9	
10	

2 **a.** Write the names of the solid shapes in these boxes.

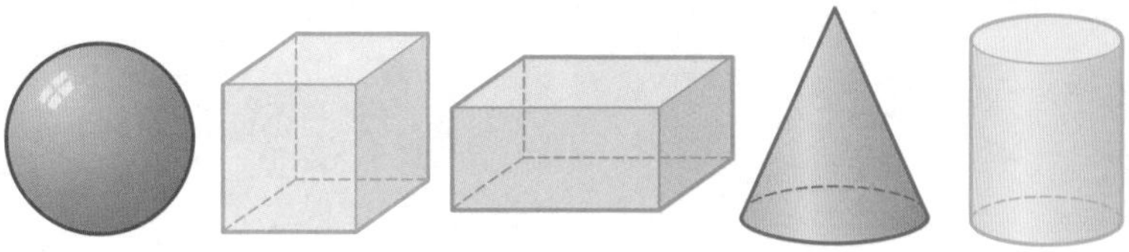

Curved face only	Flat faces only	Curved and flat faces

b. Write the names of the solid shapes in these boxes.

Corners	No corners

3 Get eight different solid shapes.
Put them on a slope.
Will the shape roll or slide?

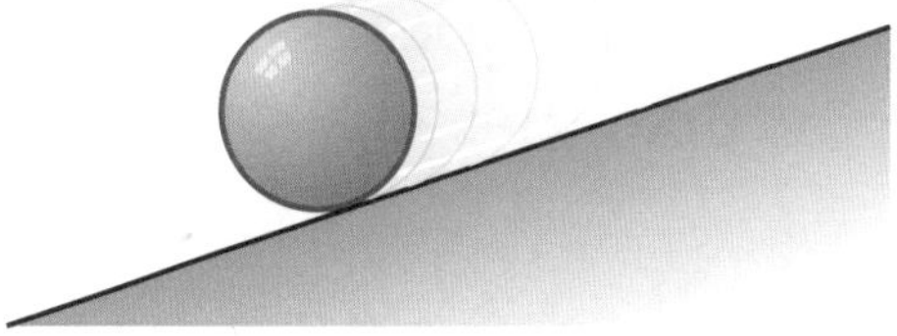

Rolls	Slides

◆ I can match 3-D solid shapes to their pictures and describe them. ☐

Let's try this!

Copy and complete these sentences.

a. A cube has ☐ square faces and ☐ corners.

b. A cuboid has 6 rectangular .... and 8 ....

c. A .... is shaped like a tin of ....

Its ends are flat c.......r.......l.......s.

6.5 Building solids

- I can build solid shapes with cubes.

Key words
cube, cuboid, face, square, solid, shapes

Get a cube.
A cube has six square faces.
You can see three faces.
But, three faces are hidden.

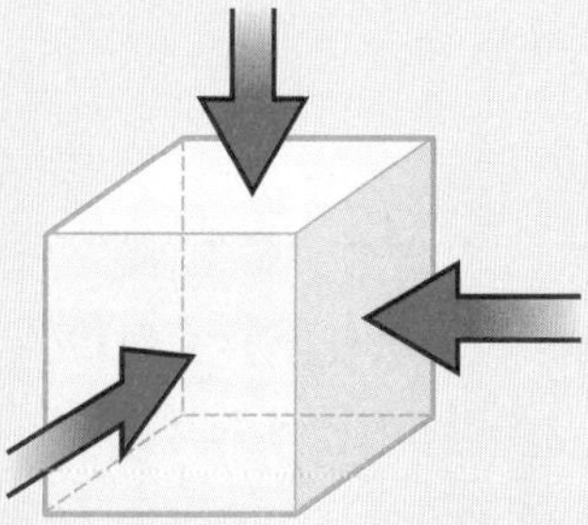

1 Get some red and blue cubes like these.

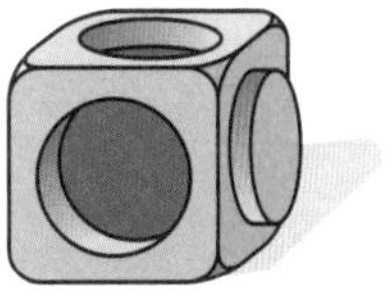

Six blue square faces

Six red square faces

Five blue square faces and five red square faces

Build these shapes using the cubes.

a.
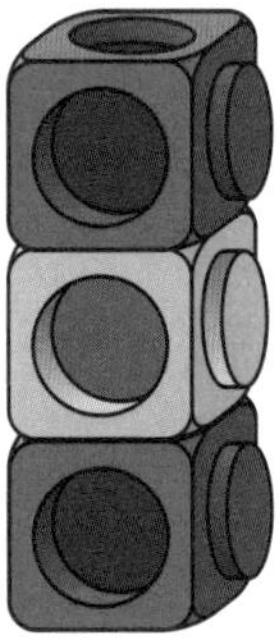

b.
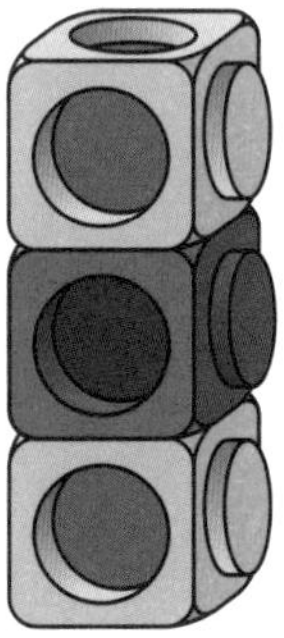

c.
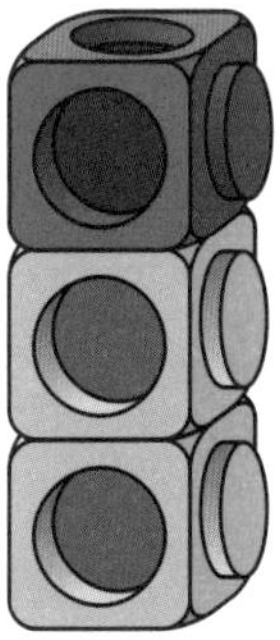

d.
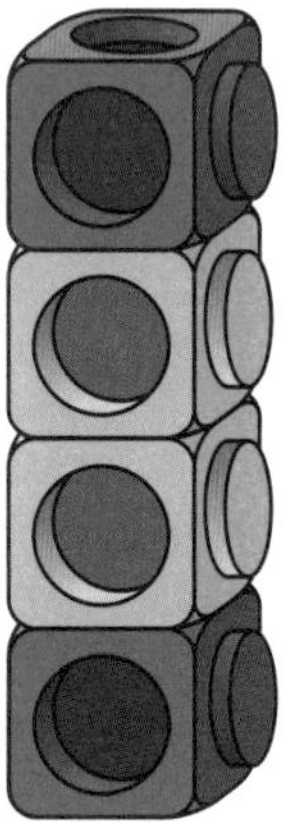

e.
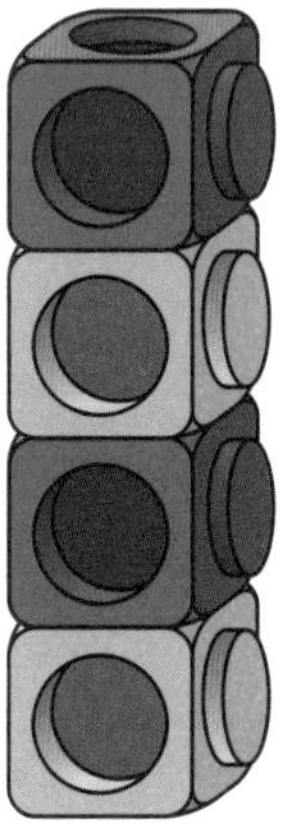

f.
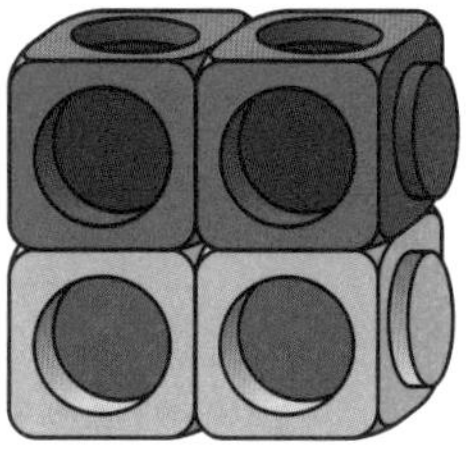

2 Count the red and blue squares in each cuboid using the shapes from Question 1.

Cuboid	a.	b.	c.	d.	e.	f.
Number of red square faces	10					
Number of blue square faces	4					

3 Get four blue, four red and four yellow cubes.
Build these shapes. Count the square faces.

a.
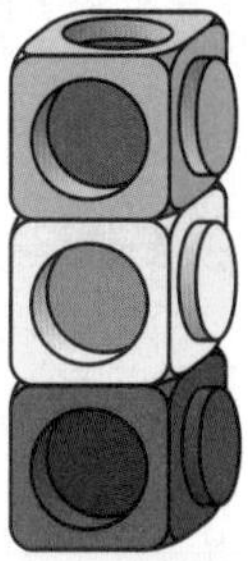
b.
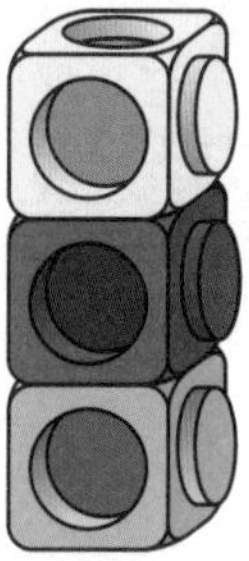
c.
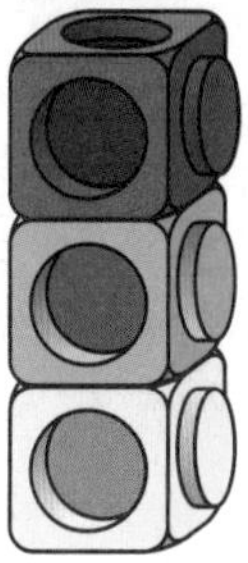
d.

Shape	Number of square faces		
	Blue	Red	Yellow
a.	5	5	4
b.			
c.			
d.			

4 Now add four green cubes.
Build these shapes. Count the square faces.

a.
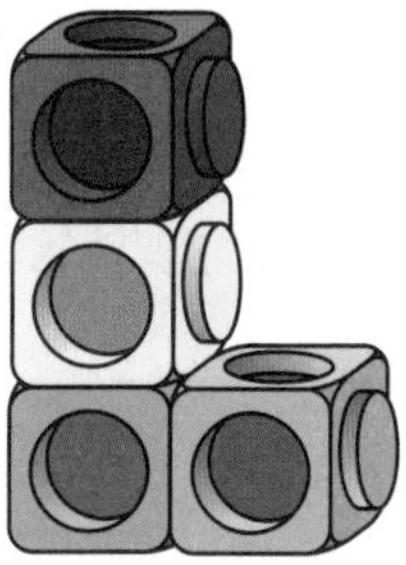
b.
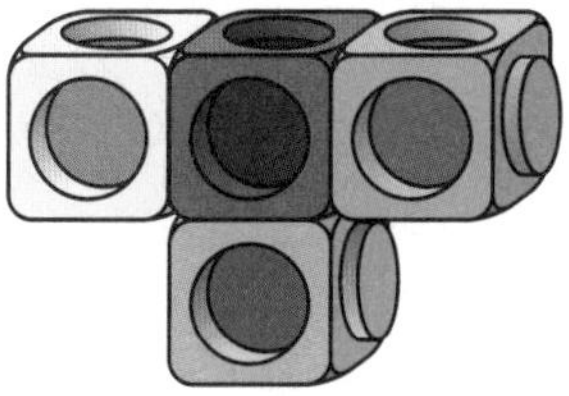
c.
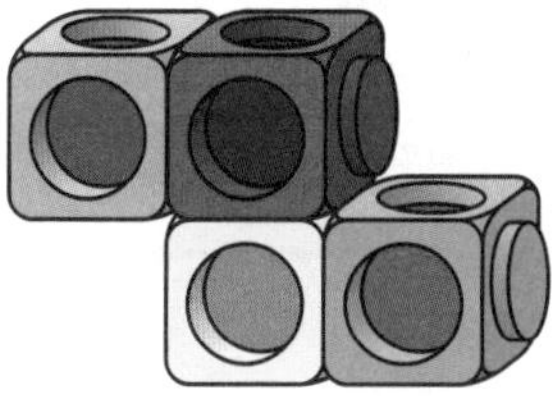
d.
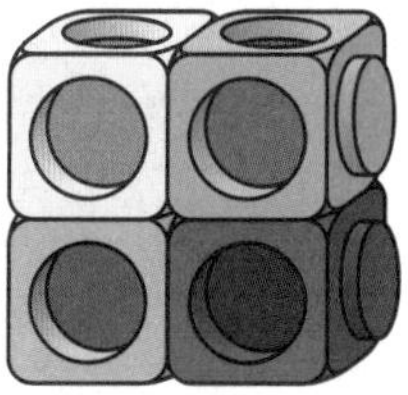

Shape	Number of square faces				Total
	Blue	Red	Yellow	Green	
a.					
b.					
c.					
d.					

◆ I can build solid shapes with cubes. ☐

Let's try this!

Build this shape. How many square faces of each colour does it have?

Multiplication and Division

7.1 Counting in twos and tens

- I can count in twos and tens.

Key words
twos, tens, count

Counting in twos and tens is very useful.
Look at the picture.
Count the children's eyes in twos.
Now count their fingers in tens.

They have ☐ eyes and ☐ fingers.

1 Practise your counting in twos.

a.

2, 4, 6, 8, 10

b.

c.

d.

e.

f.

g.

h.

2 Practise your counting in tens.
Write down the tens numbers as you count.

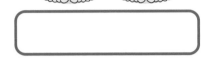

a.

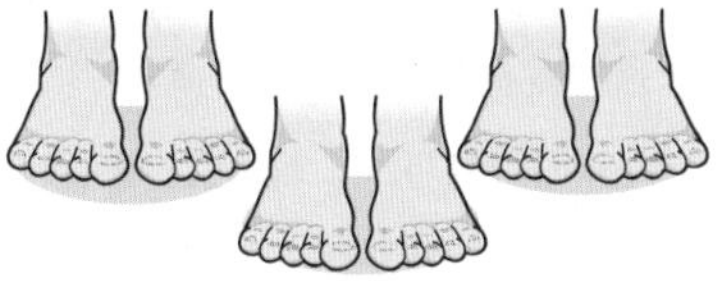

10, 20, 30

b.

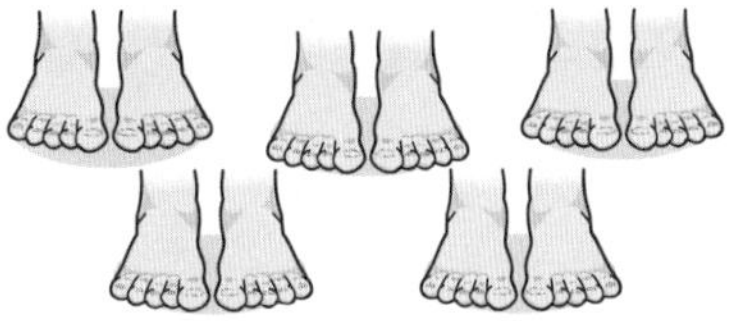

c.

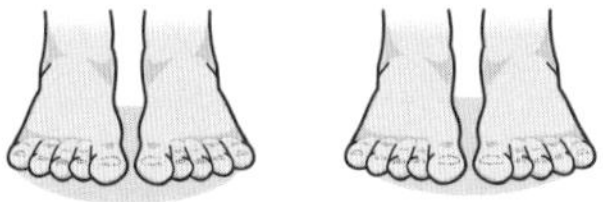

d.

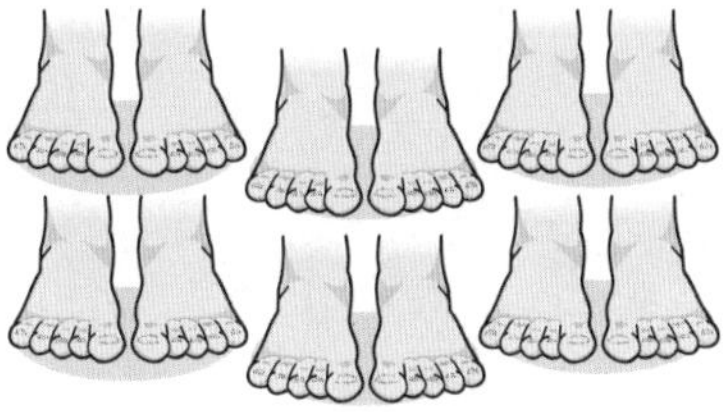

e.

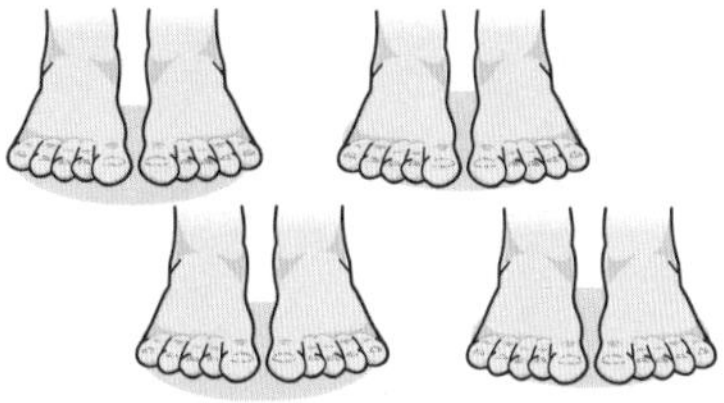

f.

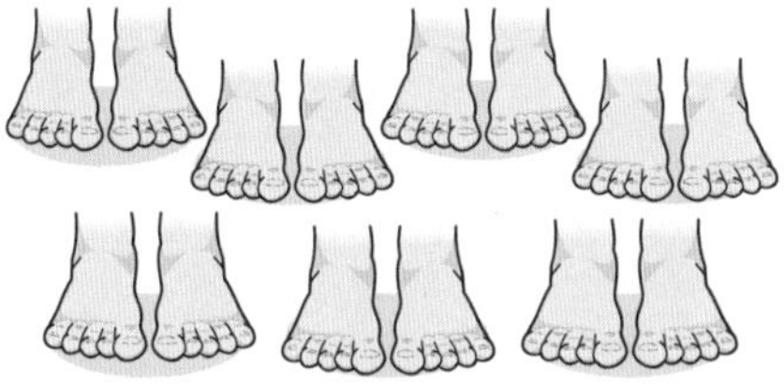

g.

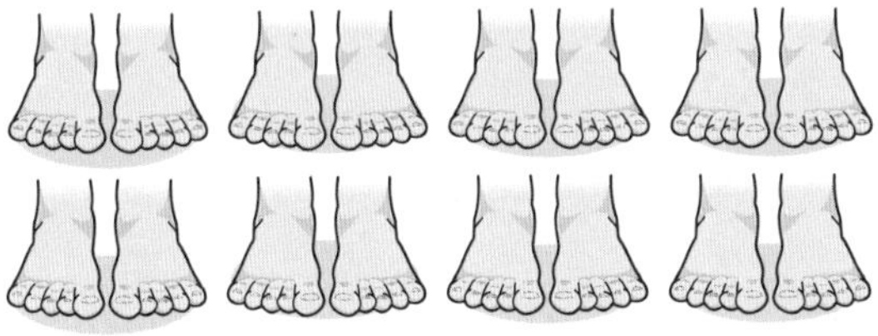

h.

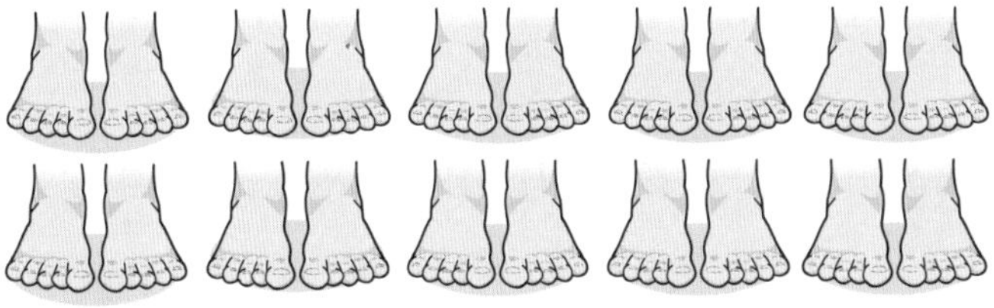

3 Circle all the numbers that you say when you count in twos.

2 12 18 8 10 5 4 16

14 11 15 6 1 7 20

4 Circle all the numbers that you say when you count in tens.

10 31 70 26 40 90 60 55

50 30 7 100 80 38 20

I can count in twos and tens. ☐

Let's try this!

Get some cards that show all the tens numbers.
Mix them up and put them in order.
What is the same about all the tens numbers?

7.2 Doubling and halving

• I can double and halve.

Key words
double, half, equal

Halving is putting a number into two equal groups.

Put these apples into two equal groups.
How many are in each group?

1 What is half of these numbers?

a. 6

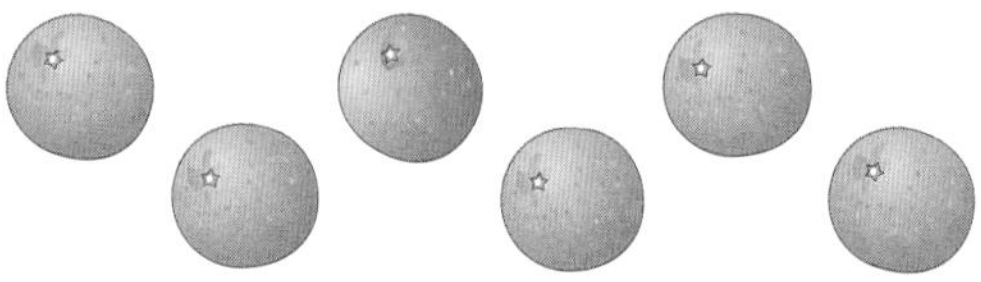

Half of 6 is [3]

b. 2

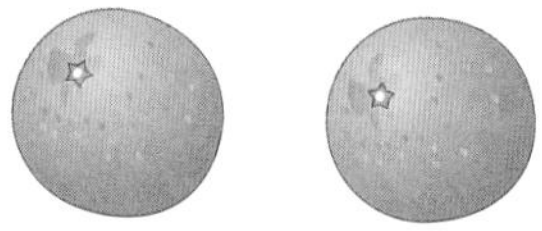

Half of 2 is [ ]

c. 10

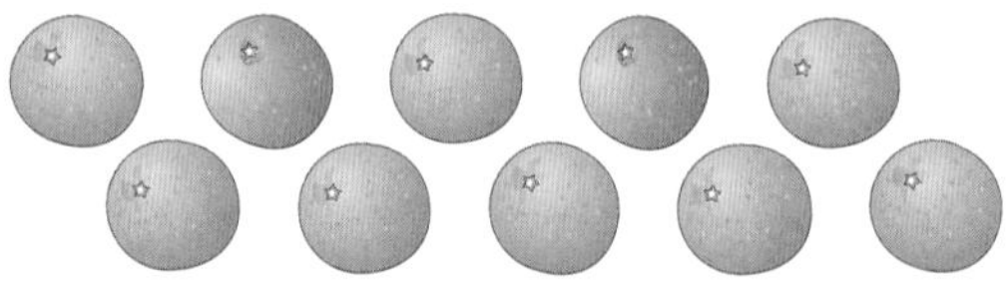

Half of 10 is [ ]

d. 4

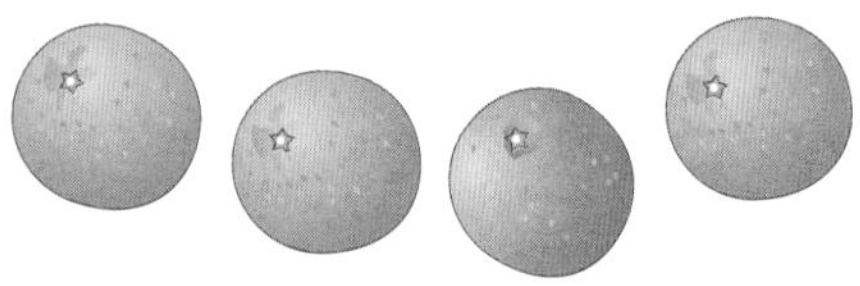

Half of 4 is [ ]

e. 12

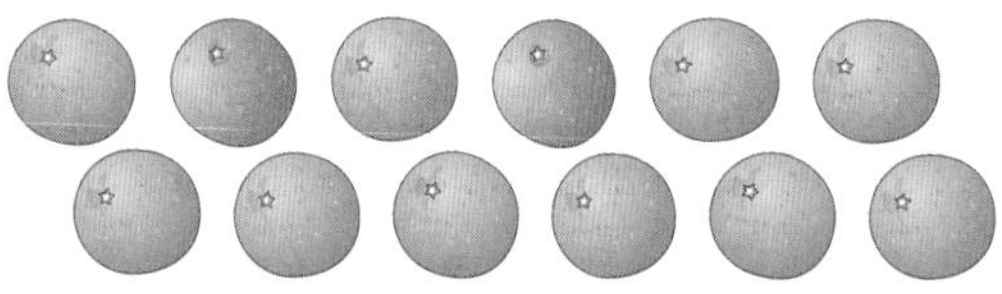

Half of 12 is [ ]

f. 8

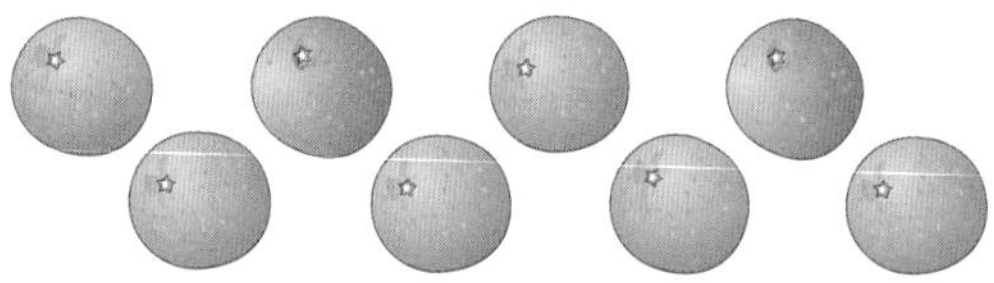

Half of 8 is [ ]

2 Fill in the halves as quickly as you can.

a.

Half of 2 is 1

b.

c.

d.

e.

f.

3 Doubling is the opposite of halving.
Fill in the missing shapes and complete the sentence.

a.
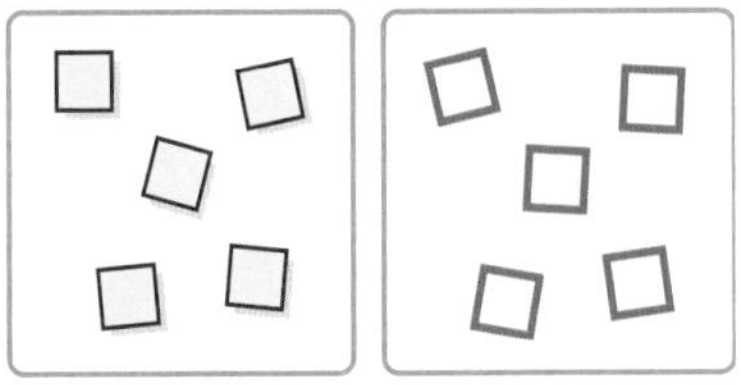
Double 5 is 10

b.
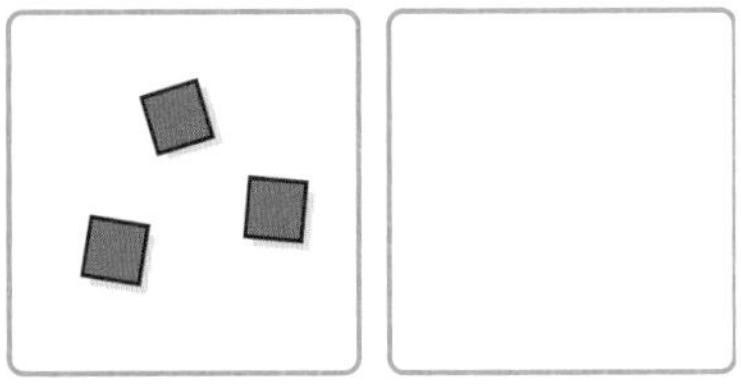
Double 3 is

c.
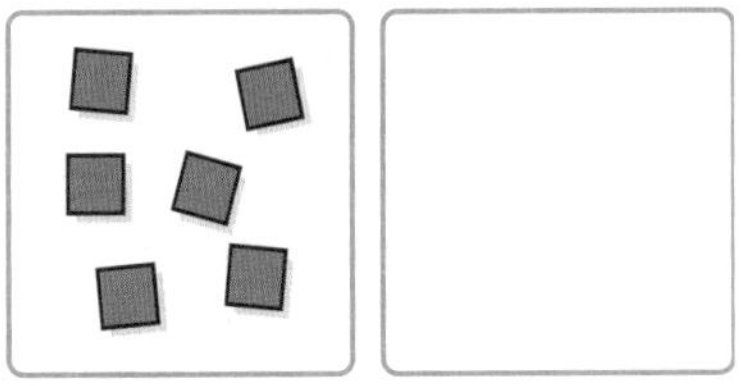
Double 6 is

d.
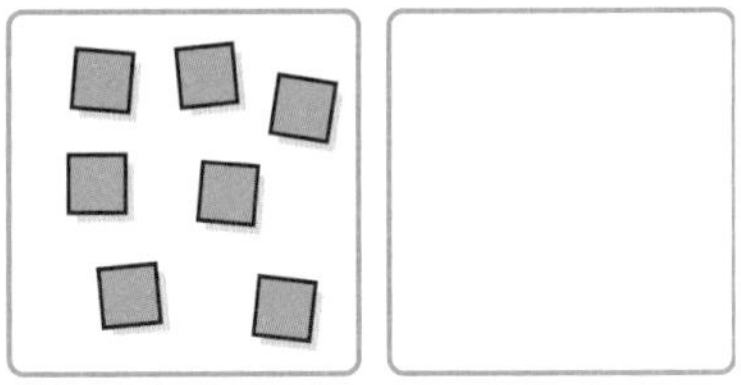
Double 7 is

e.
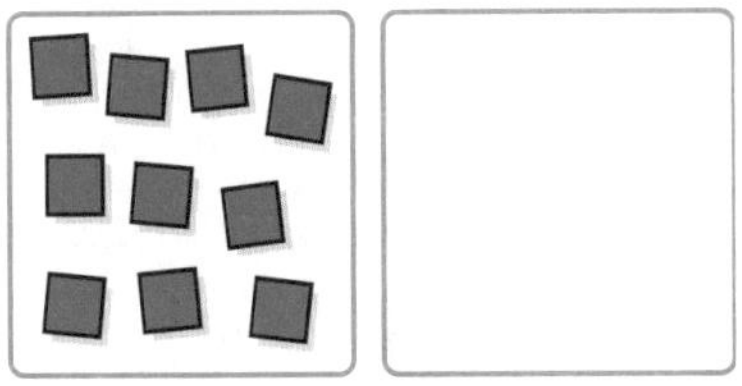
Double 10 is

f.

Double 1 is

I can work out doubles and halves.

Let's try this!

Work out half of these numbers.

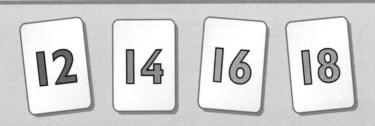

12 14 16 18

7.3 Understanding multiplication

- I can understand multiplication.

Key words
groups of, times, multiplication

Multiplication or **times** is when you have groups of the same number.

Get 20 buttons.

Put the buttons into groups of twos.

There are 10 groups of 2 or 10 times 2.

1 Draw circles around two buttons at a time to put them into groups of two. Write how many groups there are.

a.

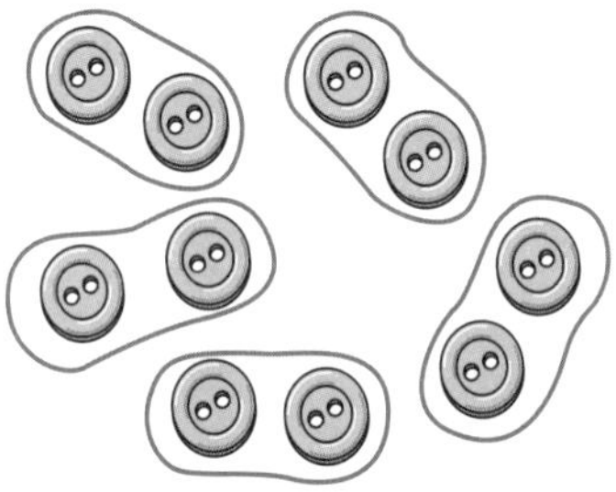

[5] groups of 2 or 5 times 2

b.

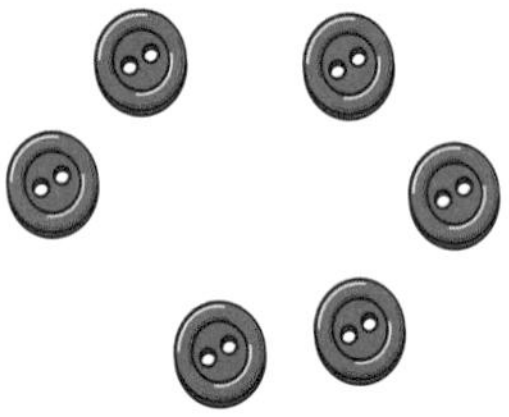

[ ] groups of 2

c.

[ ] groups of 2

d.

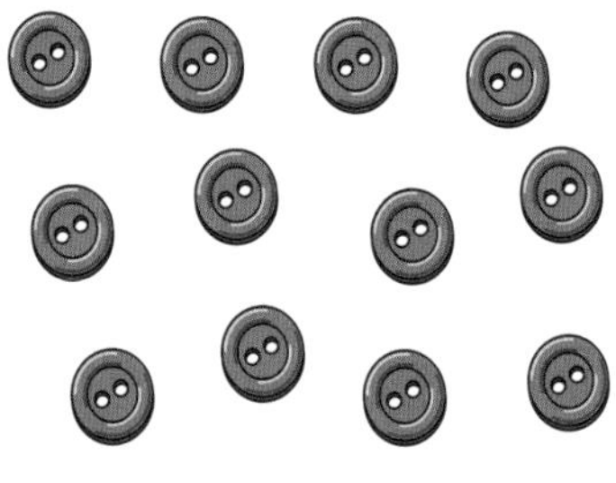

[ ] groups of 2

e.

[ ] groups of 2

f.

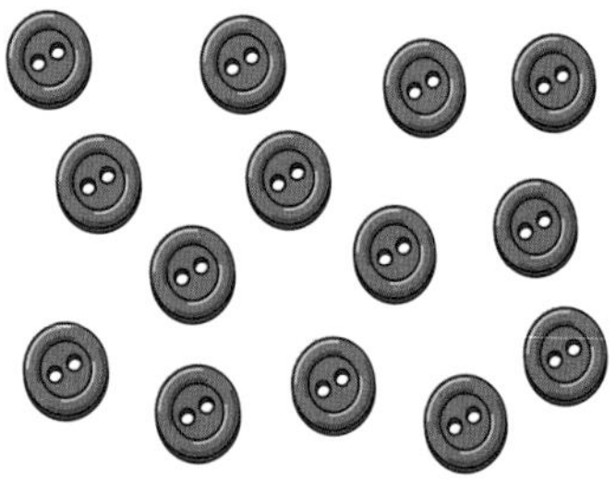

[ ] groups of 2

2 Draw buttons to go with these groups.
Then count how many there are altogether.

a. 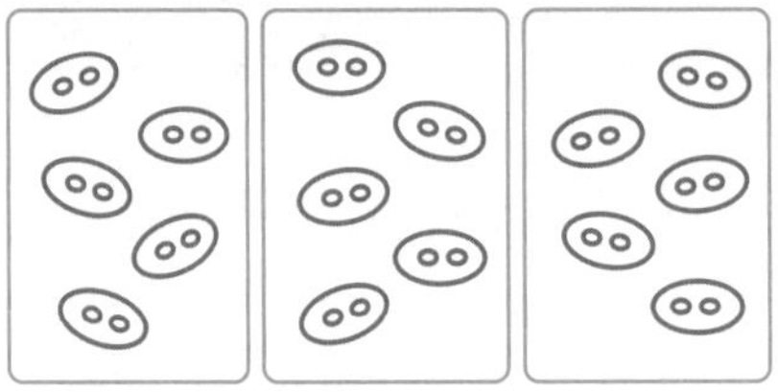 3 groups of 5 = 15

b. 2 groups of 4 =

c. 4 groups of 3 =

d. 2 groups of 10 =

e. 5 groups of 2 =

f. 4 groups of 5 =

g. 3 groups of 3 =

h. 2 groups of 6 =

i. 3 groups of 4 =

j. 6 groups of 3 =

k. Choose four questions and write them as times.

I can put numbers into groups.

Let's try this!

Draw 20 buttons. Put them into groups.
There are four different ways of doing this. Can you find them all?

7.4 Multiplication as repeated addition

- I can understand multiplication as repeated addition.

Key words
repeated addition, times, groups

Times is when you have **groups of the same** number.
You can add the numbers to find out how many you have altogether.

Get 12 buttons.

Put the buttons into **groups** of 3.

Now count them in threes.

You can write this as an addition:
$3 + 3 + 3 + 3 = 12$

This is the same as **4** groups of **3**:
$4 \times 3 = 12$

1 Write the addition sum to go with these buttons.

a. 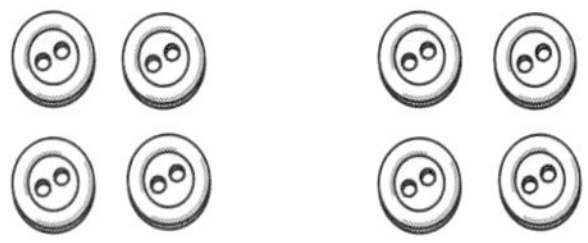

4 + 4 = 8

b. 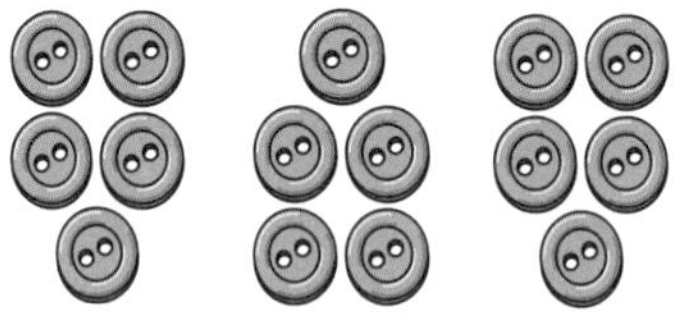

c. 

d. 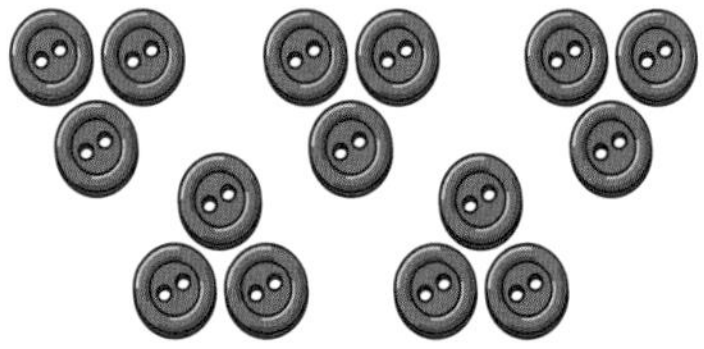

e. 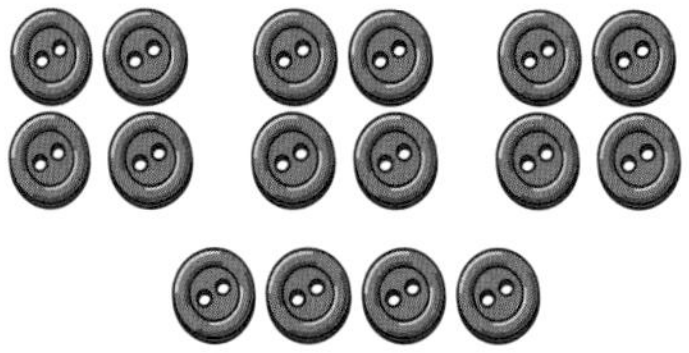

f. 

g. 

h. 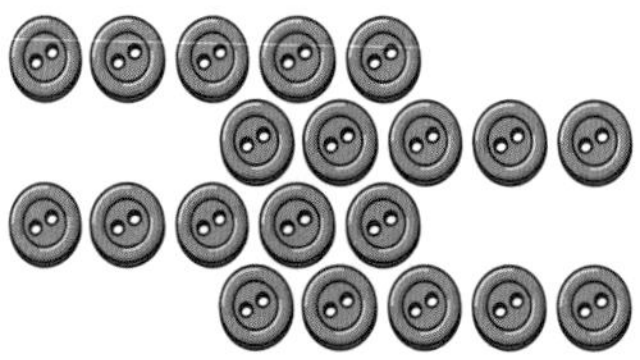

i. 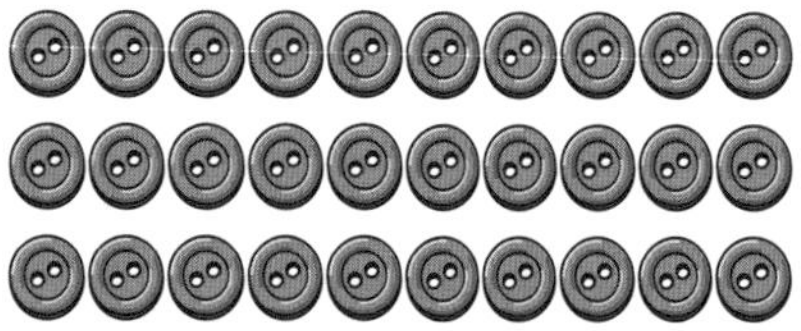

2 Look at your answers for Question 1.
Fill in the boxes to go with each one.

a. 2 groups of 4 **b.** ☐ groups of ☐ **c.** ☐ groups of ☐

d. ☐ groups of ☐ **e.** ☐ groups of ☐ **f.** ☐ groups of ☐

g. ☐ groups of ☐ **h.** ☐ groups of ☐ **i.** ☐ groups of ☐

3 Draw the groups for these additions.

a. 3 + 3 + 3 = 9 **b.** 5 + 5 + 5 = ☐ **c.** 4 + 4 + 4 + 4 = ☐

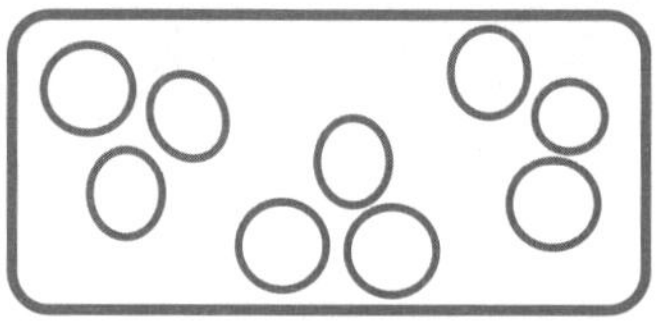

d. 2+2+2+2+2+2= ☐ **e.** 6 + 6 = ☐ **f.** 5 + 5 + 5 + 5 = ☐

g. 4 + 4 + 4 + 4 + 4 + 4 = ☐ **h.** 3 + 3 + 3 + 3 + 3 = ☐

I can use addition to work out times. ☐

Let's try this!

Look at these 15 coins.
Put them into three groups of five and draw them. Write the addition sum.
Now put them into five groups of three and draw them. Write the addition sum.
What do you notice?

7.5 Understanding division

- I can understand division as sharing.

Key words
divide, sharing

Think of division as sharing.

When you divide something, you share it into equal groups.

Get 15 counters.
Share these into three groups.

How many does each group get? ☐

I am going to share my 15 sweets with my friends.

1 Count the sweets. Share them between the bags.

a.  5 each

b.  ☐ each

c.  ☐ each

d.  ☐ each

e.  ☐ each

f.  ☐ each

g.  ☐ each

2 Can the apples be shared fairly between the bowls – yes or no? Remember they must all have the same number of apples.

a.

No

b.
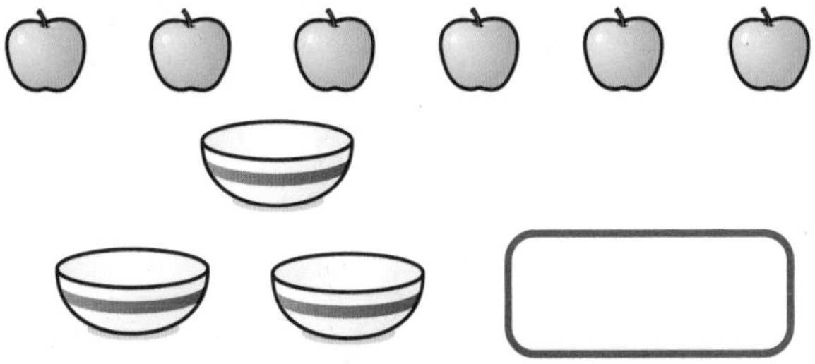

c.

d.
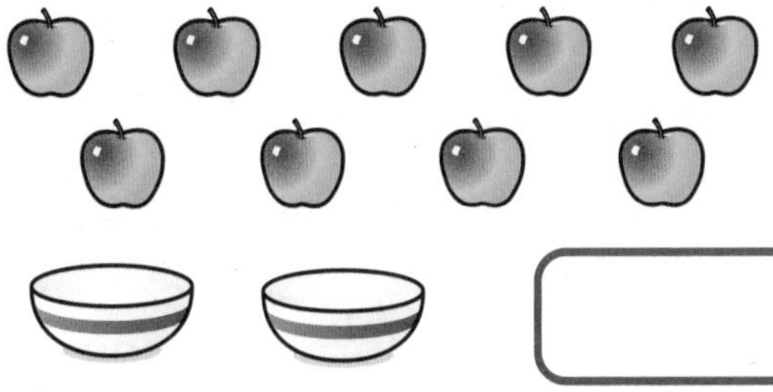

e.

f.

g.

h.

i.

j.

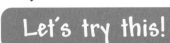

◆ I can share objects equally. ☐

Let's try this!

Lee has three apples to share between him and his friend. How can he do this?

Handling Data

8.1 Shopping lists

- I can make lists and tables of information.

Key words
information, list, table, block graph

1 **a.** Write down 10 things you want to buy.

1.
2.
3.
4.
5.
6.
7.
8.
9.
10.

b. How many tins, packets and bags did you buy?

Food	Number
Tins	
Packets	
Bags	

c. The 5th food I bought was ....

d. The last food on my list was ....

e. I bought more packets than ....

2

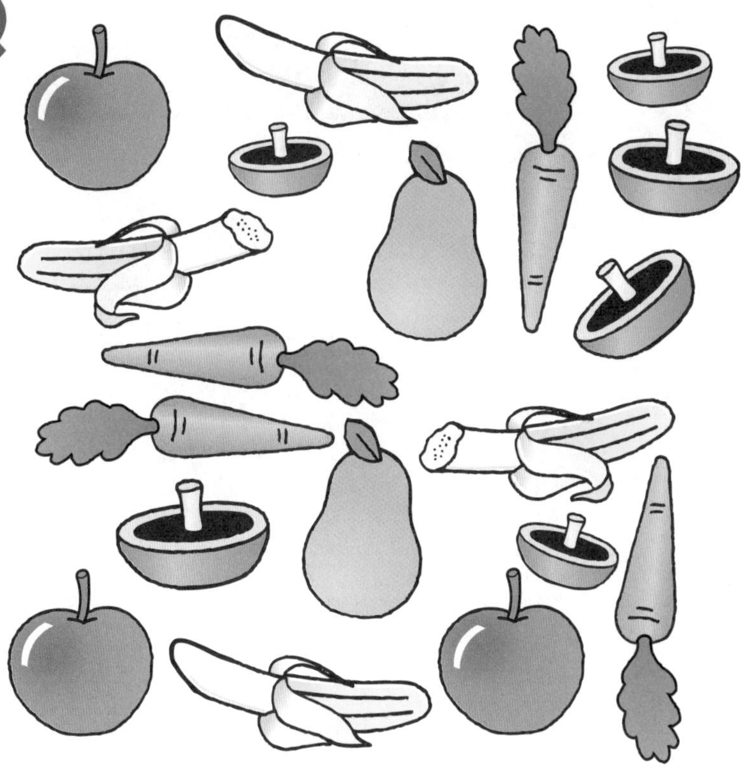

a. Look at this picture and fill in the shopping list.

Shopping list

☐ apples

☐ bananas

☐ pears

☐ mushrooms

☐ carrots

b. The 3rd item on the shopping list is ....

c. There are ☐ fruits. There are ☐ vegetables.

◆ I can organise information on lists and tables. ☐

Let's try this!

In the block graph, colour a square for each fruit or vegetable shown in Question 2.

There are ☐ more mushrooms than bananas.

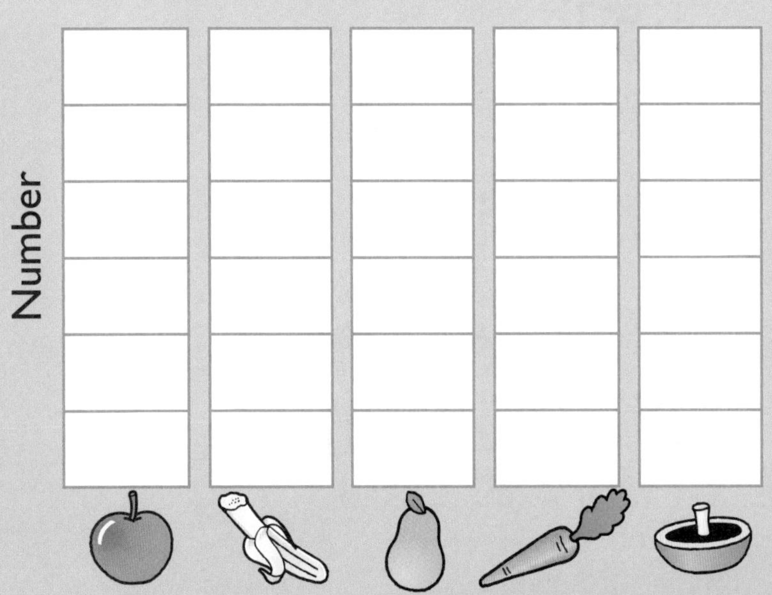

8.2 Keeping a tally

- I can use tally marks to keep a score.

Key words
count, tally, table,
most common, least common

Long ago people counted in 5s because there are five fingers on each hand.

Then people used tally sticks for numbers.

To record tallies, they drew one line for each thing and made bundles of five.

The fifth thing was shown as a line across the other four lines.

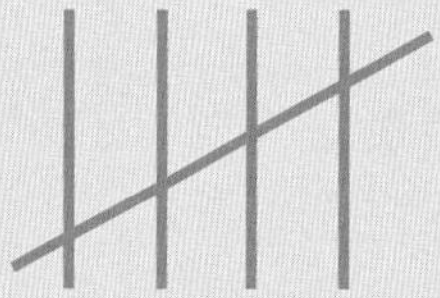

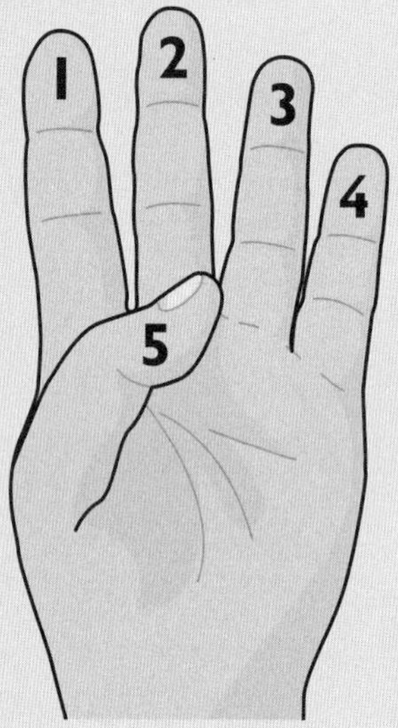

1 **a.** Write each tally as a number.

Tally	Number
𝍷𝍷𝍷𝍷	4
𝍸 𝍷	
𝍸 𝍷𝍷𝍷	
𝍸 𝍸 𝍷𝍷	
𝍸 𝍸 𝍸 𝍷𝍷𝍷𝍷	
𝍸 𝍸 𝍸 𝍸	

b. Write each number as a tally.

Number	Tally
3	
7	
10	
13	
15	
18	

2 Get a box full of 40 counters in three colours – red, blue and green.
Pick a counter from the box.
For each counter you pick make a tally mark in the table.
Carry on until the box is empty. Work out the total for each colour.

Colour of counter	Tally	Total
Red		
Blue		
Green		

3 Using your table from Question 2, fill in these gaps.

a. There are ☐ red counters. There are ☐ blue counters.

b. The least common colour is ....

I can use tally marks to keep score. ☐

Let's try this!

Get 50 interlocking cubes in four colours.
Use all the cubes to build a wall five cubes high.
Now, take away one cube at a time and say its colour.
Make a tally mark in the table. Do this for all the blocks in the wall.

Colour of cube	Tally	Total

Find the total number of cubes for each colour and write it in the table.

The most common colour of cube is ☐ .

8.3 Sorting diagrams for shapes

- I can sort objects and use diagrams to show how they were sorted.

Key words
sort, count, diagram, block graph, least common

1. Count the numbers of each shape and write them in this table.

Shape	Number
Circle	
Triangle	
Square	

2. For each shape, put a tick in the sorting diagram.
Count the ticks.
Write the total number in the circles.

	Orange	Not orange
Squares	✓✓ (2)	◯
Not squares	◯	◯

	3 sides	Not 3 sides
Blue	◯	◯
Not blue	◯	◯

3

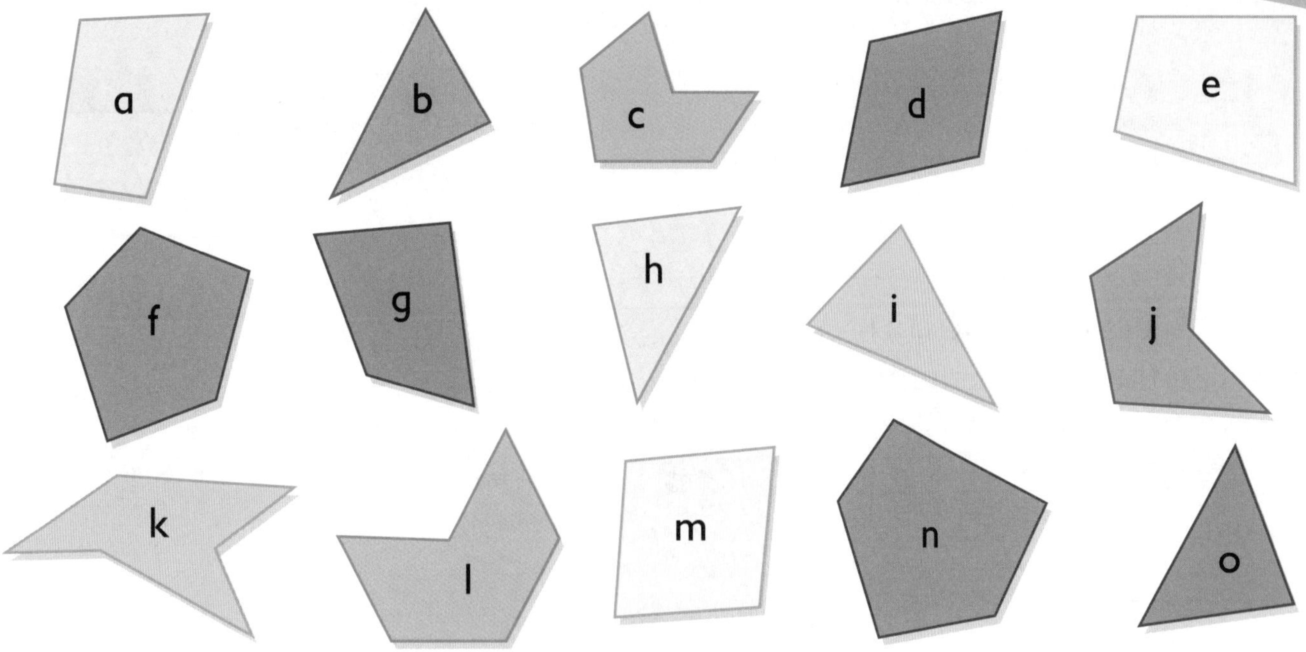

For each shape, count the number of sides and write its letter in the box.
Write the total number of each shape in the small box.

3 sides	4 sides	5 sides	6 sides

I can use diagrams to show how objects are sorted. ☐

Let's try this!

Shape					
Number	4	8	6	3	5

For each chocolate, colour a square in the block graph.

The least common shape is ....

My favourite shape is ....

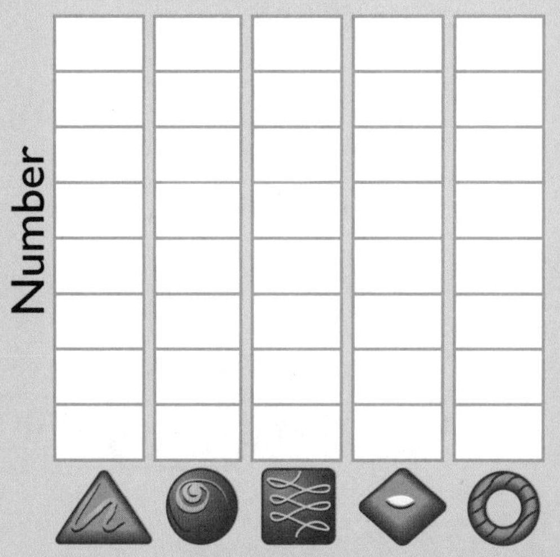

8.4 Using pictographs

- I can show information in a diagram, tally chart or pictograph.

Key words
tally, pictograph

Put the eggs in the correct pans.
Write the correct numbers inside the pan.

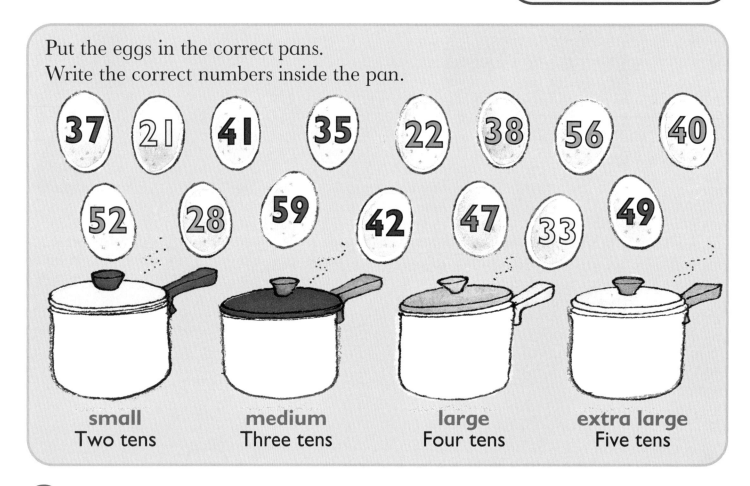

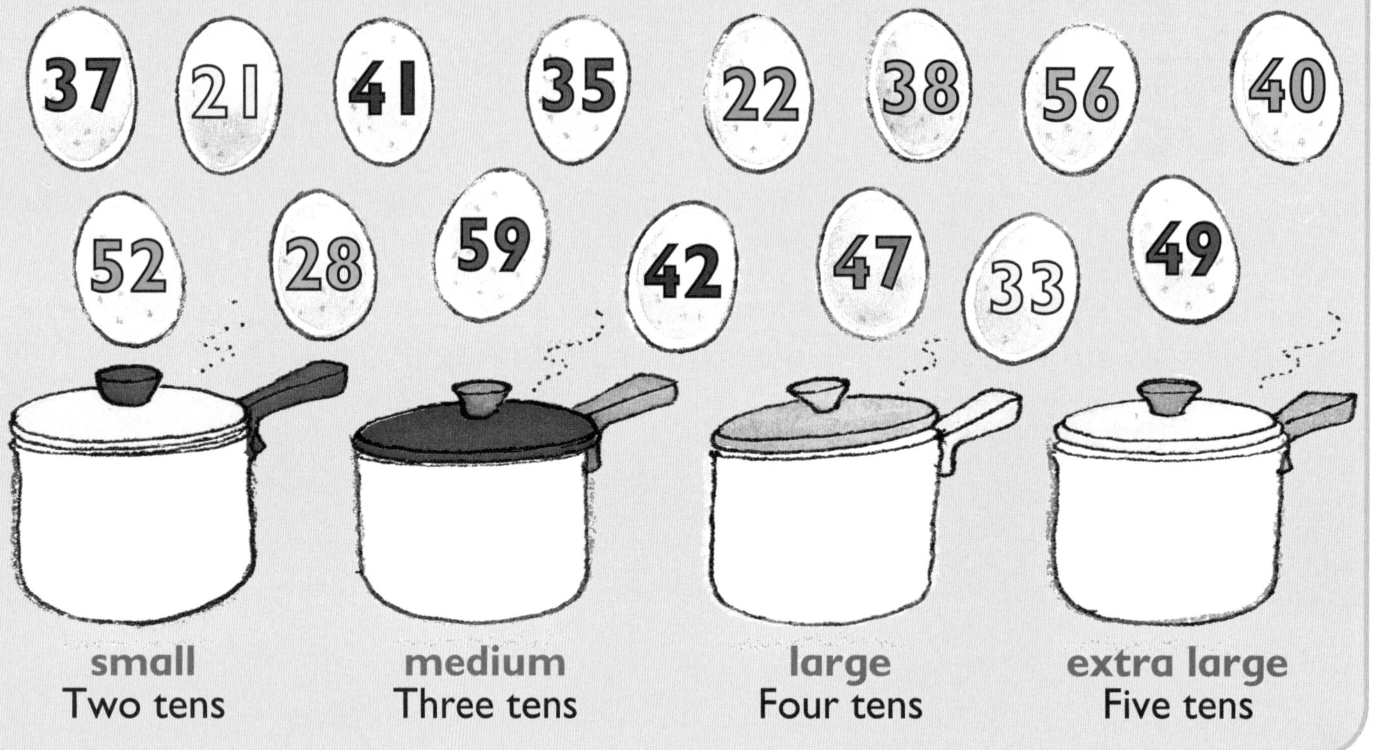

1 Now look at the numbers inside the pans above.

For each egg, draw an oval shape in the pictograph.

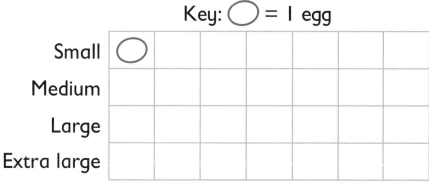

Key: ◯ = 1 egg

Small	◯						
Medium							
Large							
Extra large							

Number of eggs

There are ☐ more large size eggs than small size eggs.

3 Peter is a keen pool player.
These are the balls he potted in two of his games.
Make a tally mark for each ball colour.

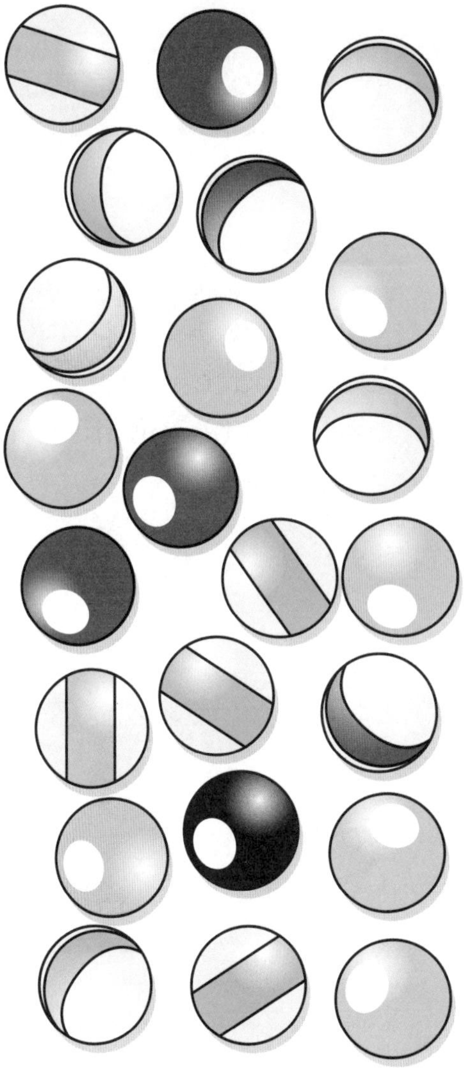

Colour	Tally	Total
Black		
Blue		
Green		
Red		
Yellow		

3 For each ball Peter potted, draw a circle in the pictograph.

Key: ◯ = 1 ball

Peter's games of pool

Black							
Blue							
Green							
Red							
Yellow							

Number of balls potted

◆ I can show information in a tally chart or pictograph. ☐

Let's try this!

Play this dice game with a partner. Each player makes a copy of the grid on squared paper.

- Take turns to roll the dice.
- Colour a square in the grid for each score.
- The winner is the first person to complete a row of six squares.

⚀						
⚁						
⚂						
⚃						
⚄						
⚅						

8.5 Sorting coins

- I can use diagrams to sort objects and make a block graph.

Key words
sort, count, diagram, block graph, pictogram

Get some real 1p and 2p coins.
Cover each copper coin with a real coin showing either heads or tails.
Slide each coin into either the heads or tails money box.

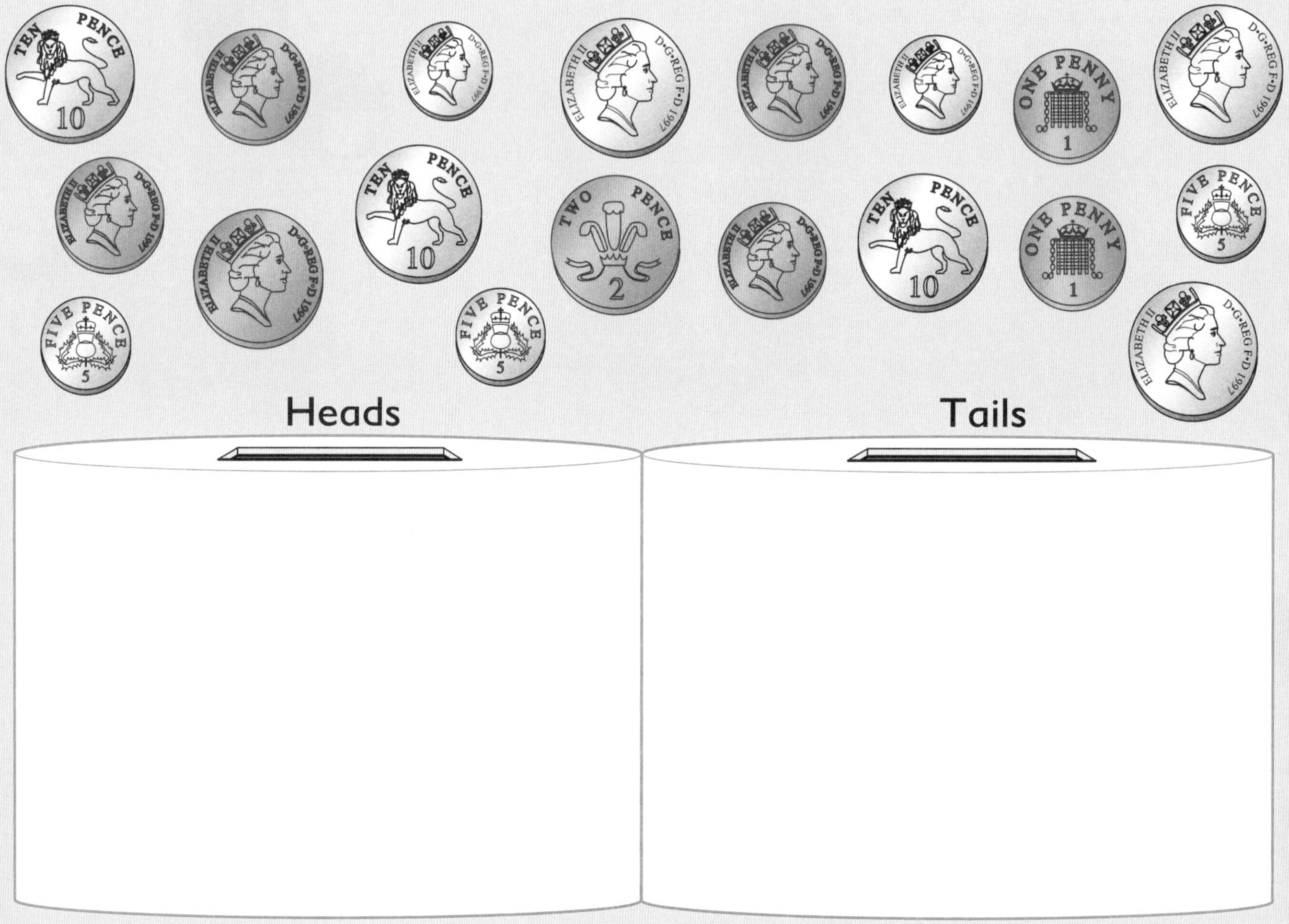

1 Now look at the coins inside the money boxes. Fill in the blanks.

a. ☐ 1p coins show tails. **b.** ☐ 2p coins show heads.

c. There are ☐ copper coins altogether.

2 Look at the coins on page 82.

a. Put a tick in the sorting diagram for each silver coin. Count the ticks. Write the total in the circles.

	Heads	Tails
5p	◯	◯
10p	◯	◯

b. There are ☐ silver coins that show heads.

c. There are ☐ silver coins that show tails.

3 The coins on the page 82 show how much money Sandra has in her purse.

a. Fill in the block graph.

b. The least common coin is worth ☐ p.

c. Sandra has ☐ p in 1p and 2p coins.

Coins in Sandra's purse

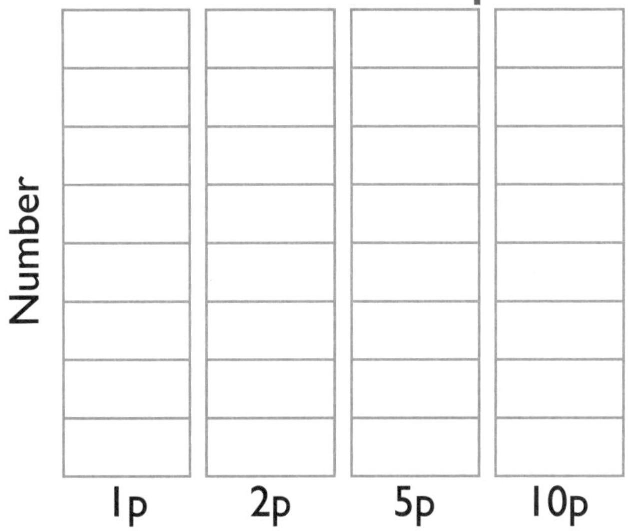

◆ I can use diagrams to sort objects and make a block diagram. ☐

Let's try this!

Make a pictogram about the coins in Sandra's purse. Draw a circle for each coin in the pictogram.

Sandra has ☐ p in silver coins.

Key: ◯ = 1 coin

1p							
2p							
5p							
10p							

More on Shapes

9.1 Draw a line of symmetry in 2-D shapes

- I can draw the line of symmetry on a shape.

Key words
shape, line of symmetry, fold, mirror line

This is a balanced shape. The two halves match. The fold line is called the line of symmetry.

It is also called the mirror line.

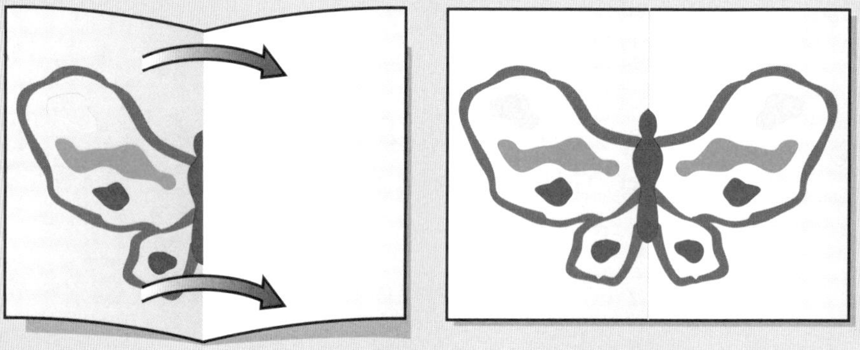

1 On each flag draw the lines of symmetry.

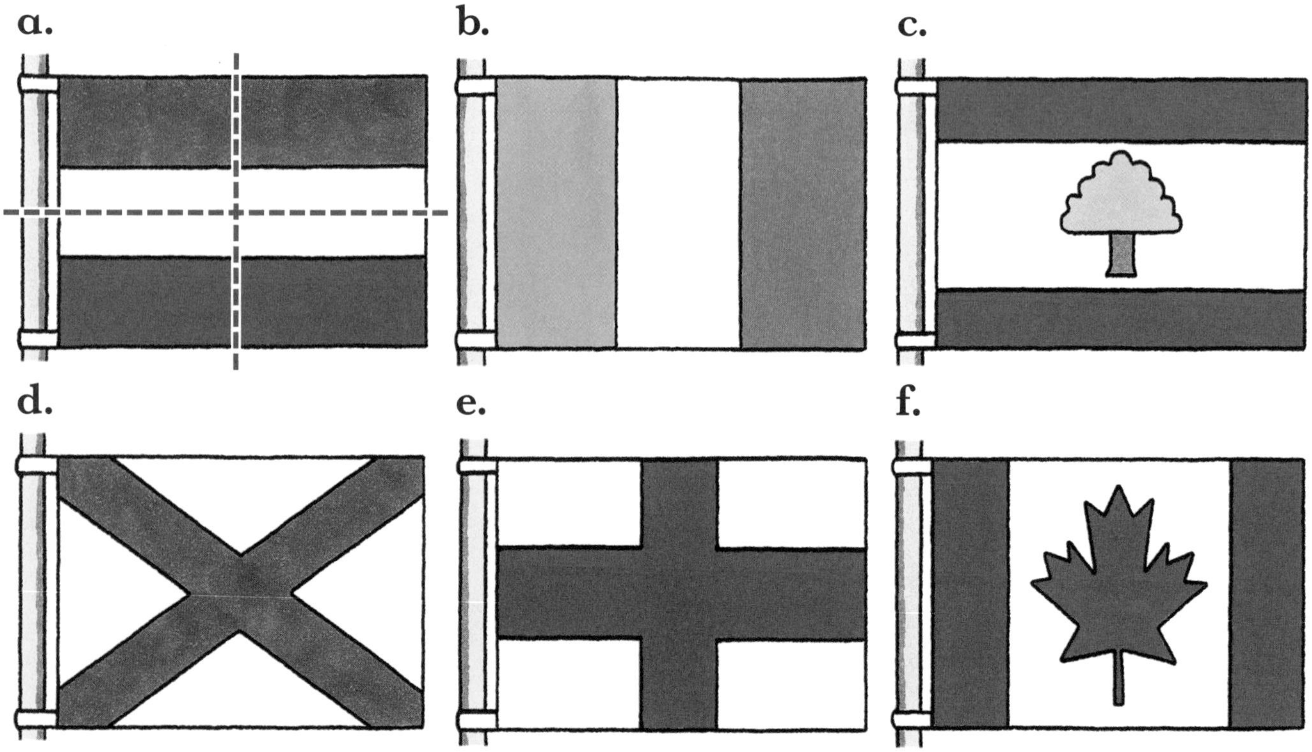

2 Draw the mirror lines with a pencil and a ruler.
Colour half of the shape.

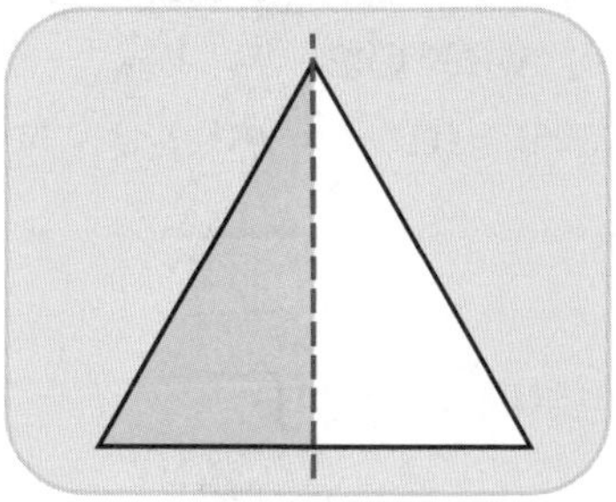

a.

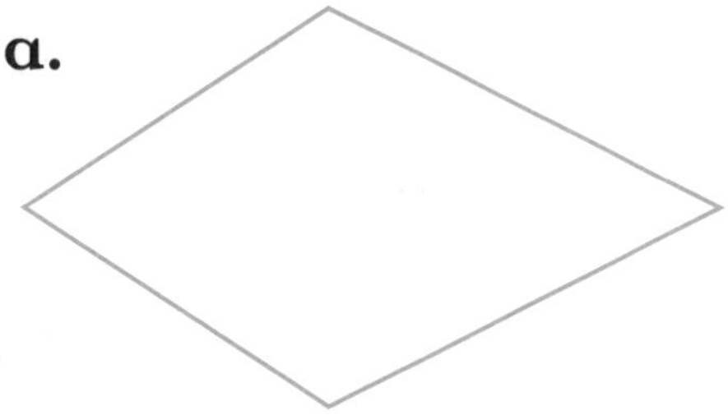

b.

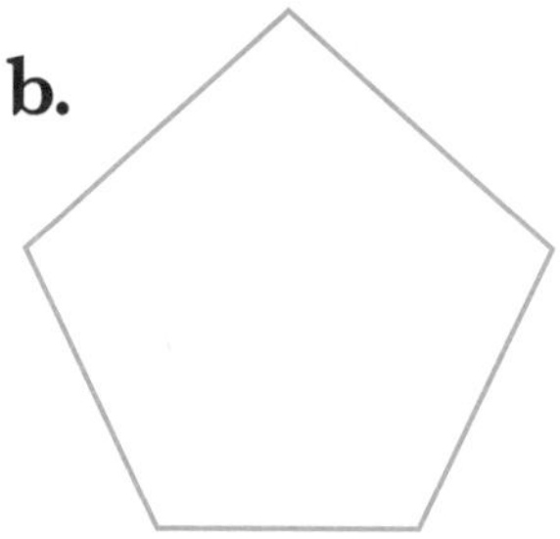

c.

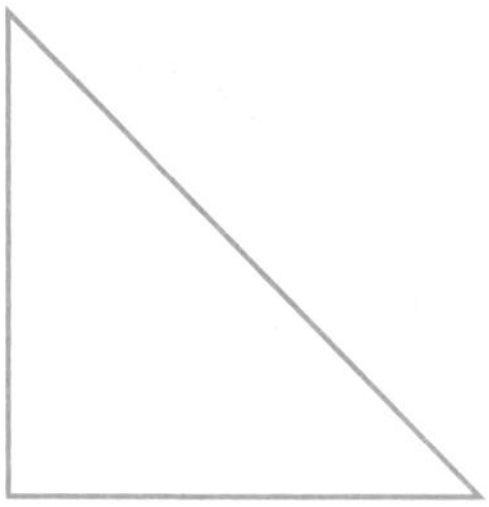

d.

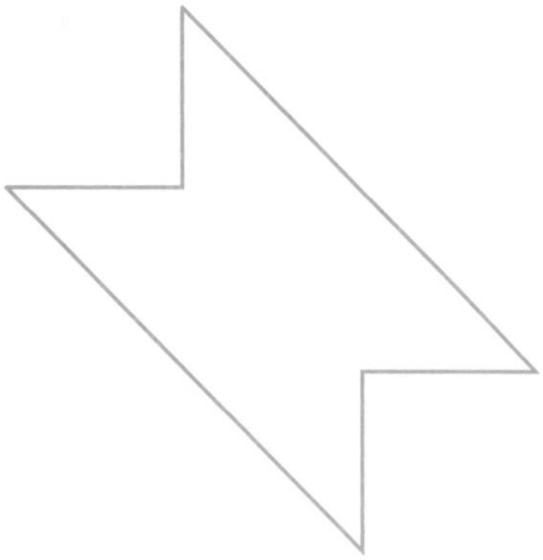

e.

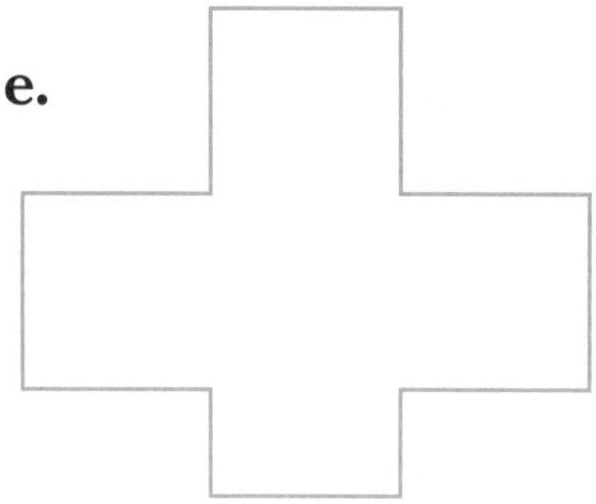

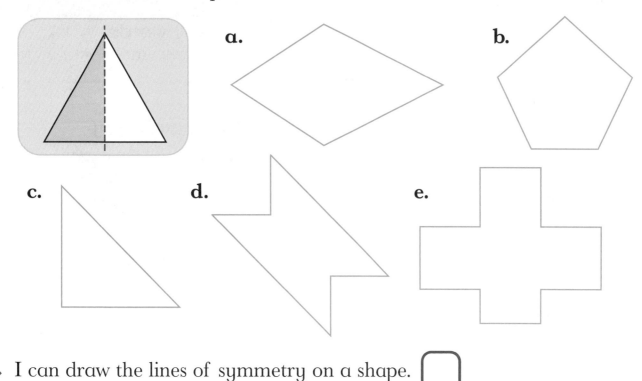

I can draw the lines of symmetry on a shape. ☐

Let's try this!

Get a strip of paper, scissors and a pencil.

1. Fold your strip of paper to make a zigzag.

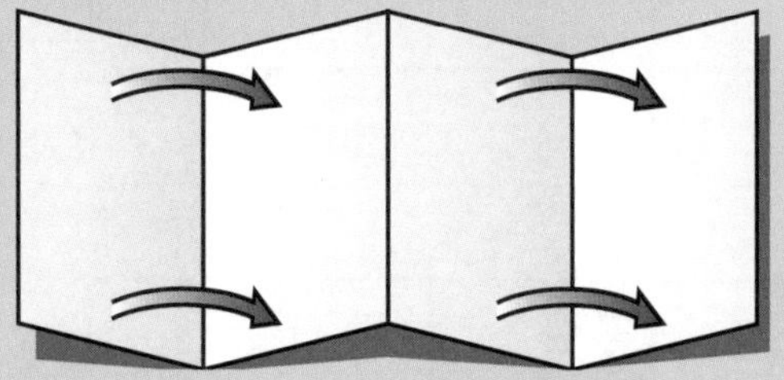

2. Fold the zigzag in half.

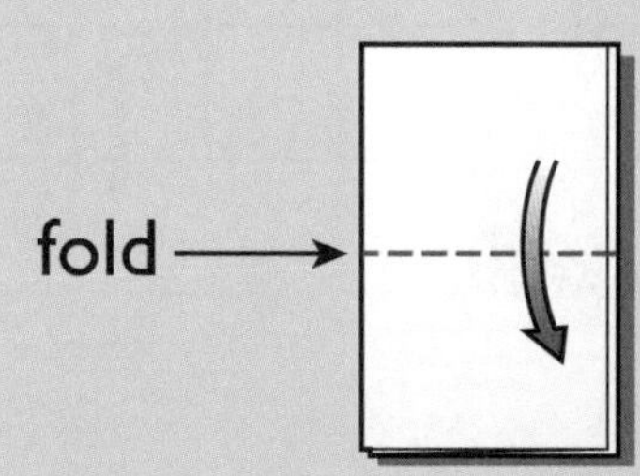

3. Draw a shape and cut it out.

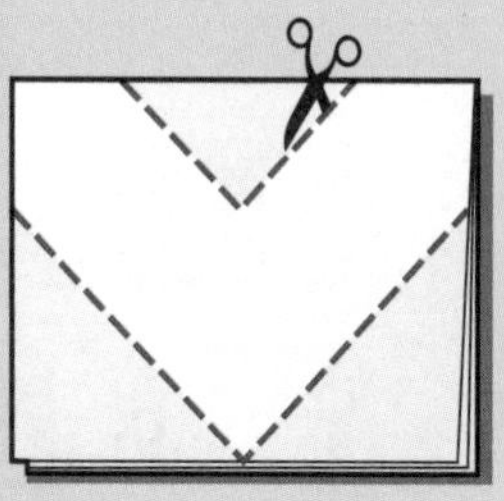

4. Open out your strip of paper and draw all the lines of symmetry.

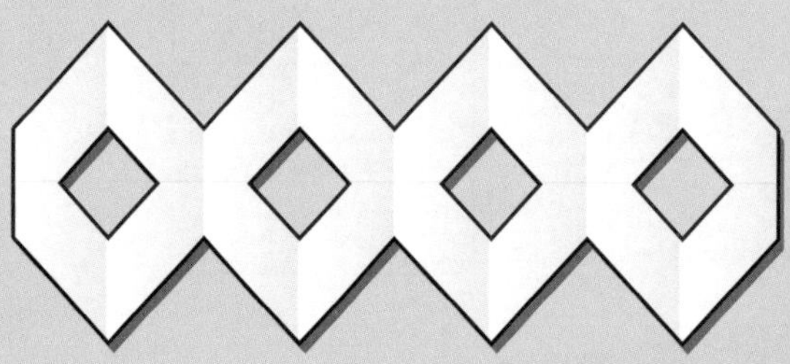

9.2 Complete a symmetrical picture

- I can draw the missing half to make a symmetrical pattern.

Key words
shape, line of symmetry

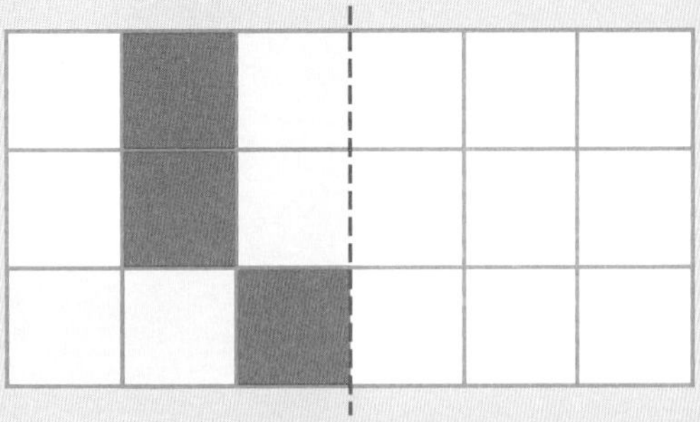

This is half of a symmetrical pattern.

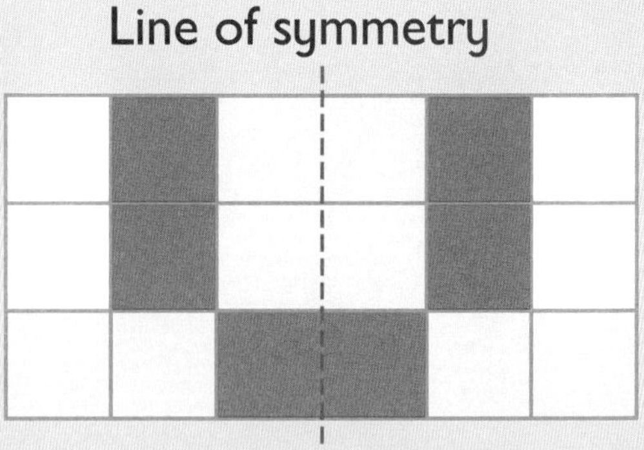

This is the whole symmetrical pattern.

1 Get some coloured pencils.
Finish each pattern by colouring the matching half shape.
You may use a mirror.

a.

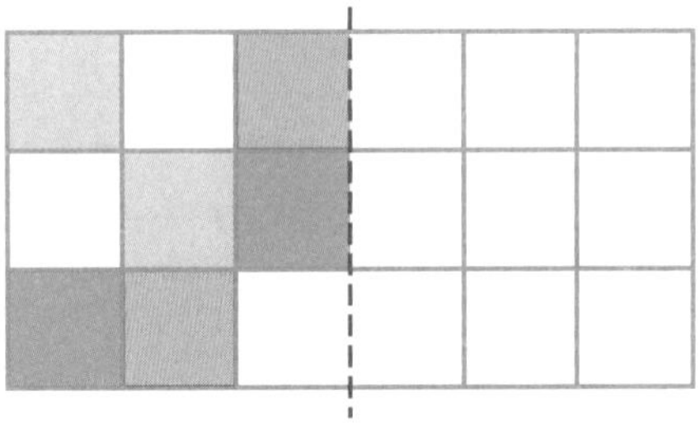

b.

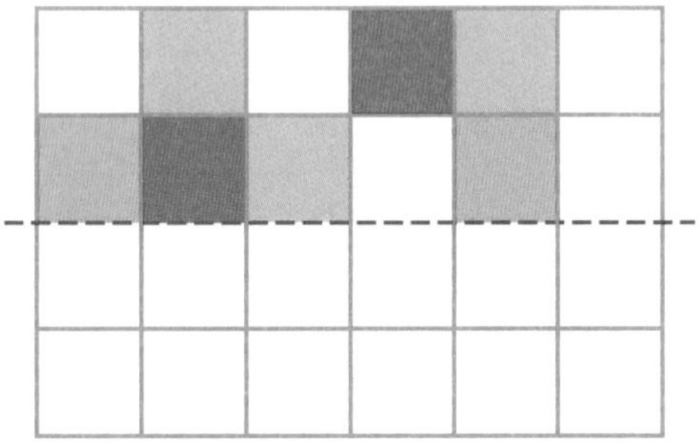

c.

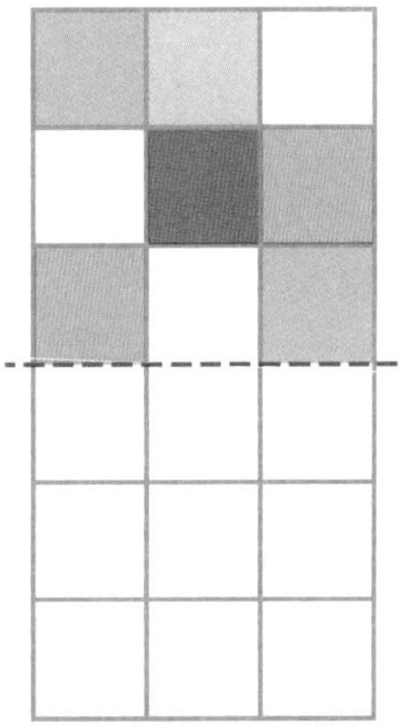

d.

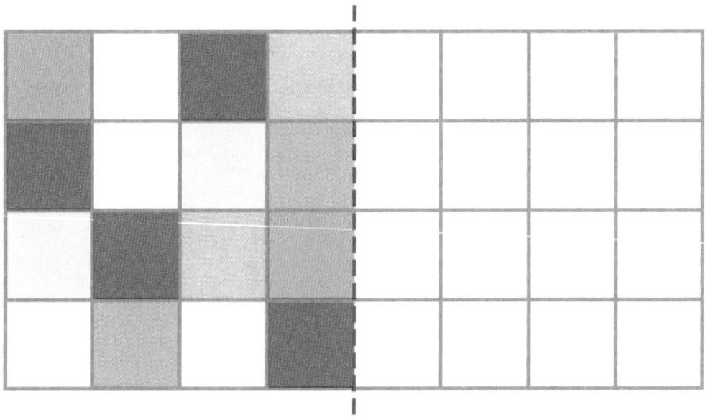

2 Finish each pegboard pattern by colouring the matching half.
You may use a mirror.

a.

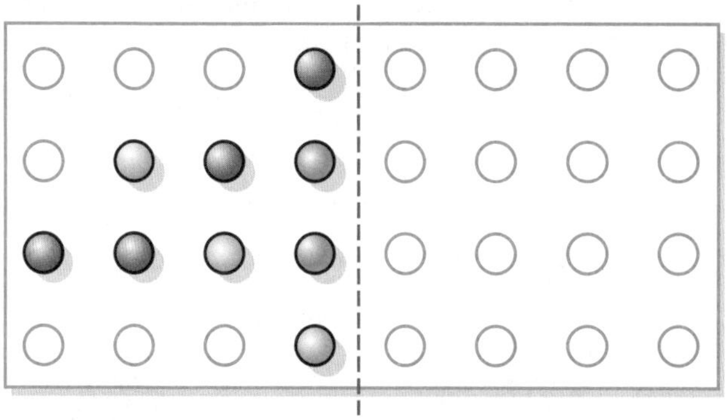

b.

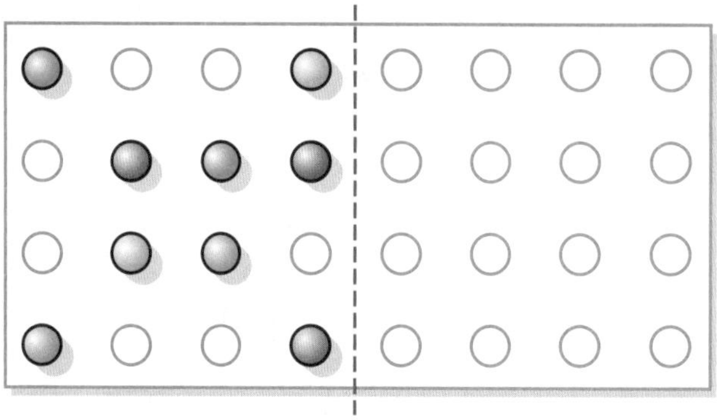

3 Finish the symmetrical butterfly patterns using coloured pencils.

a.

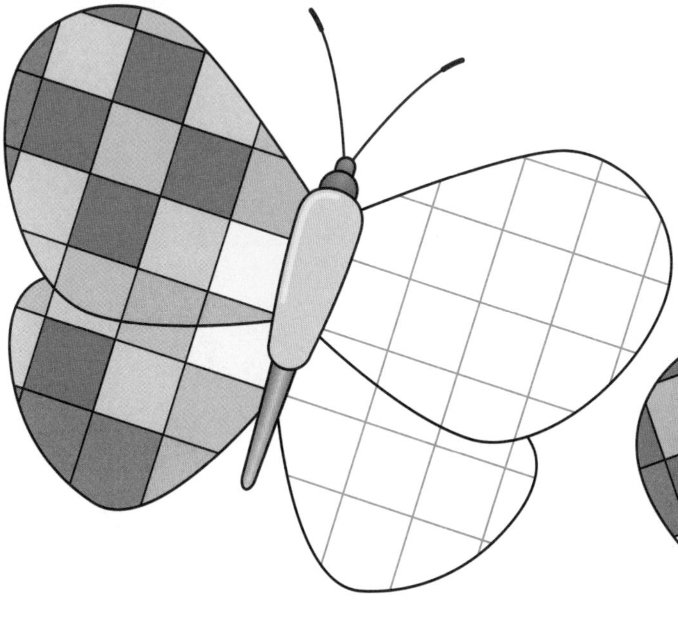

b.

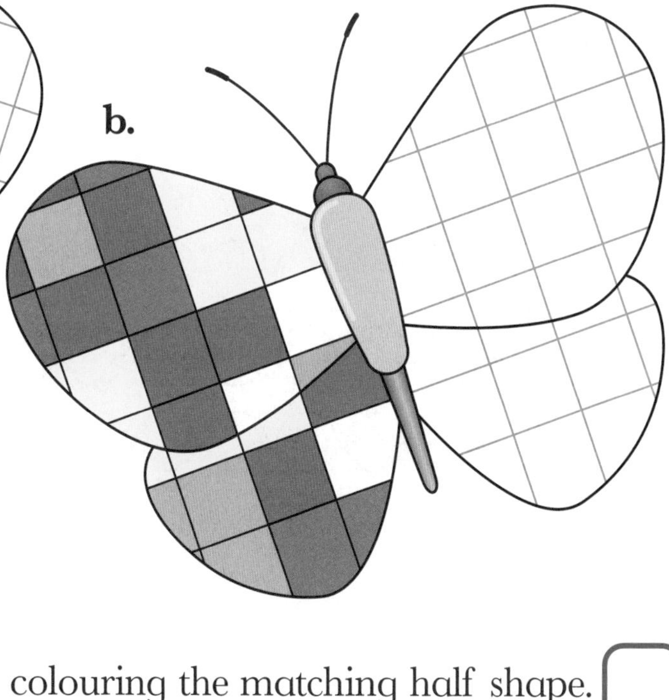

◆ I can make a symmetrical pattern by colouring the matching half shape. ☐

Let's try this!

Find a picture of a butterfly.
Copy and colour the picture to show its symmetry.

9.3 Repeating patterns of shapes

- I can continue a pattern for a set of shapes and colours.

Key words
shape, pattern, repeat, quarter turn, half turn

You can make a pattern:

- by repeating colours.

- by repeating shapes.

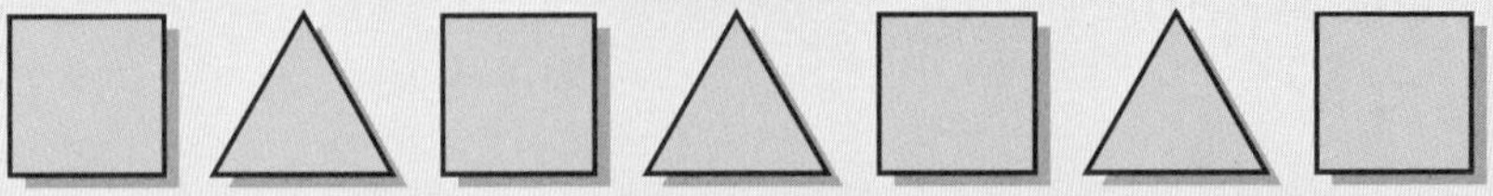

- by making a half turn of a shape.

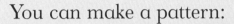

1 Continue the patterns as far as you can go. Use coloured pencils.

a. Patterns with beads

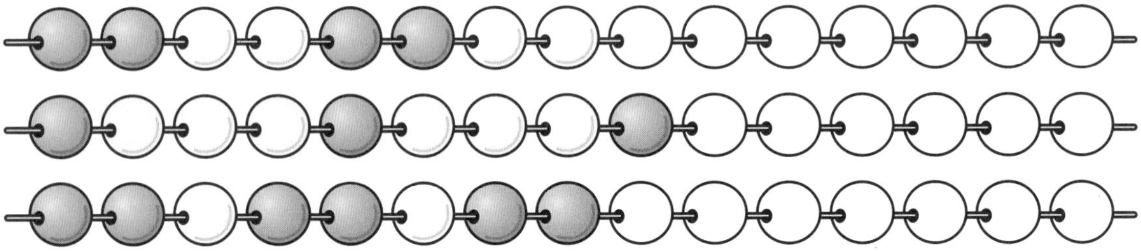

b. Patterns with shapes

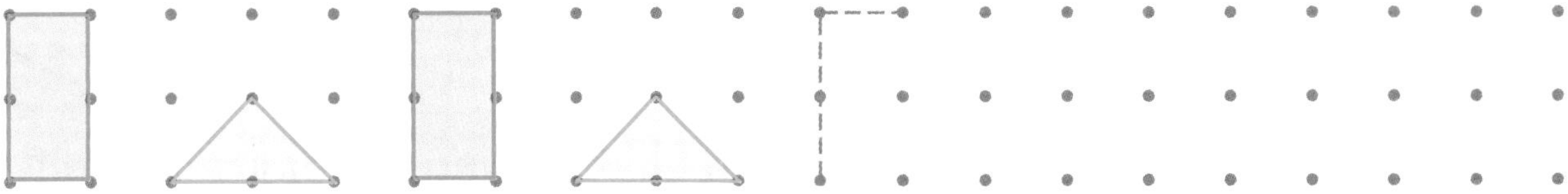

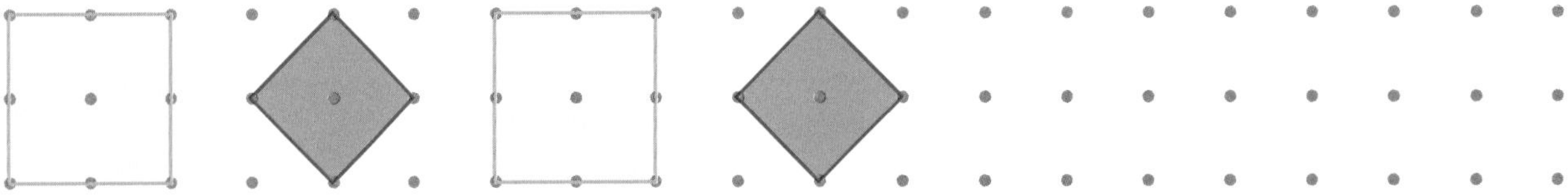

2 Continue these patterns.

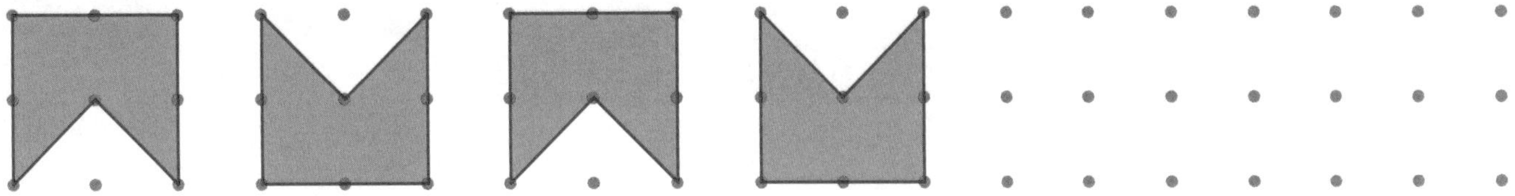

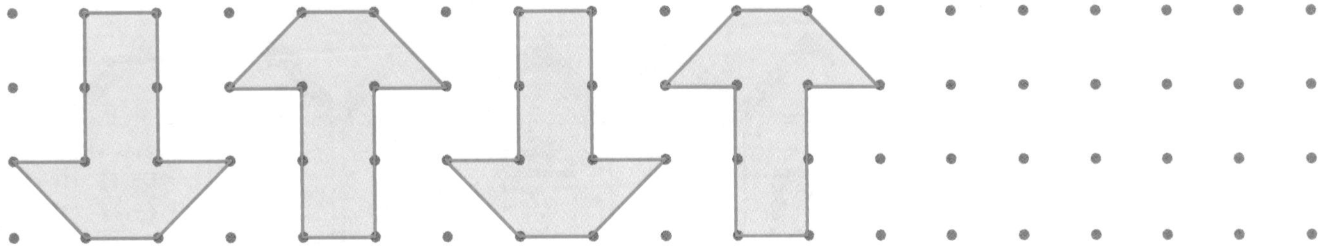

3 Finish these quarter turn patterns.

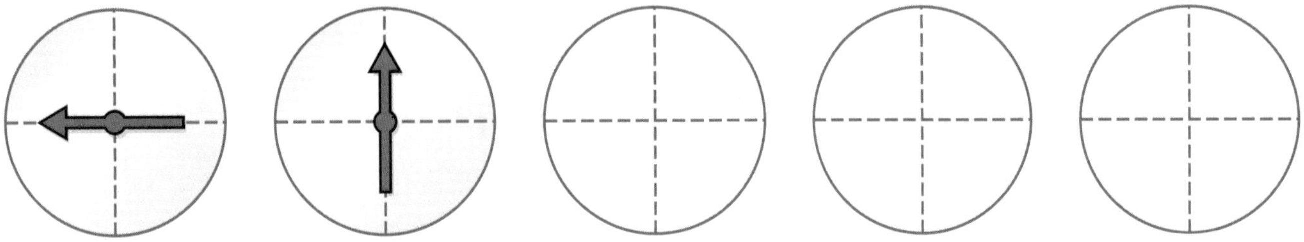

I can continue a pattern for a set of shapes or colours. ☐

Let's try this!

These patterns are made with half turns.
Fill in the missing patterns.

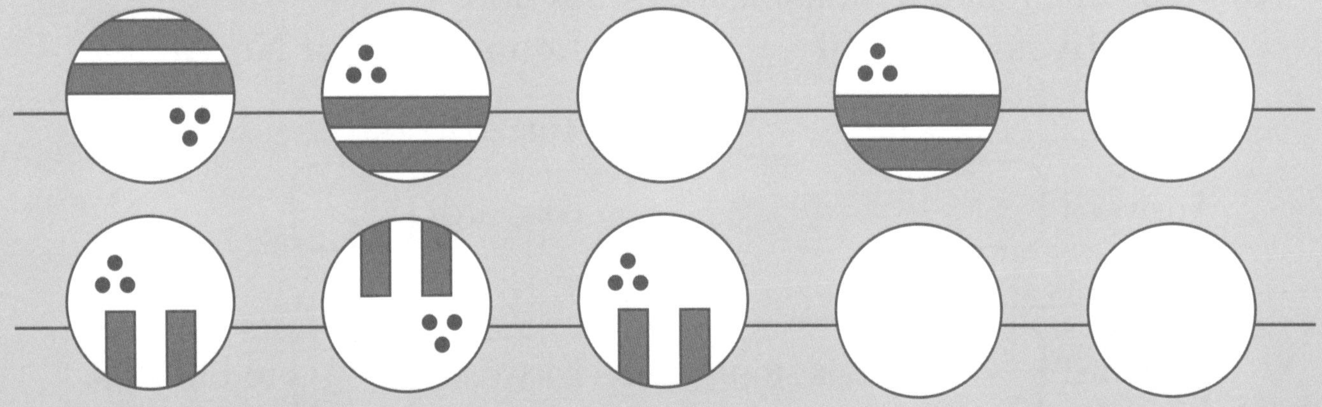

9.4 The way home

- I can give and follow instructions to move along a route.

Key words
route, turn, left, right

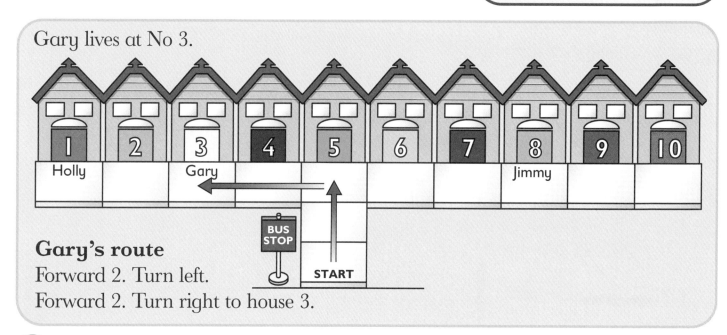

Gary lives at No 3.

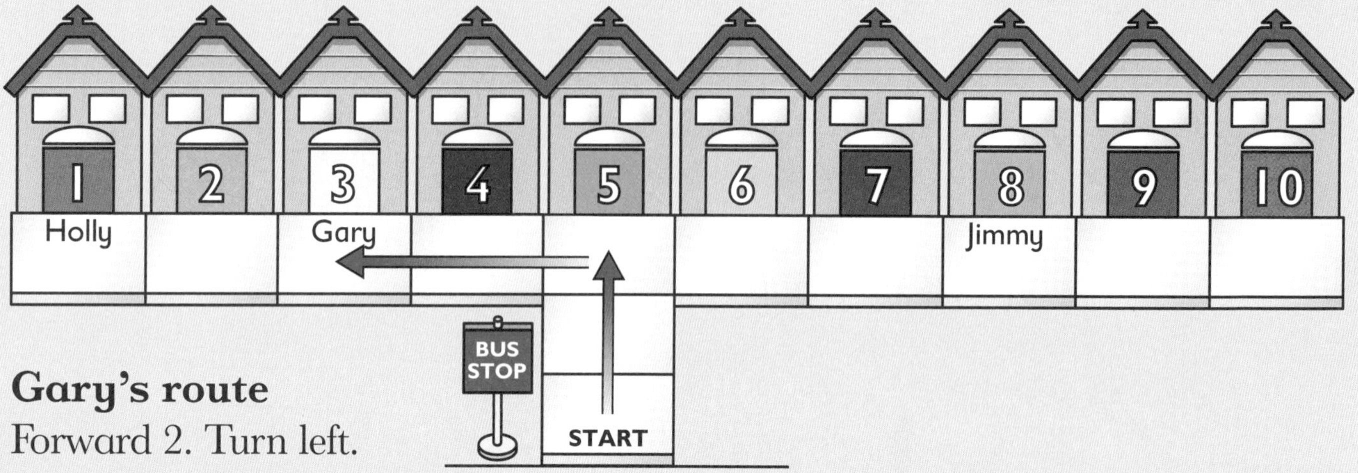

Gary's route
Forward 2. Turn left.
Forward 2. Turn right to house 3.

1 **a.** Write the routes from the bus stop to home.

Holly's route

Forward ☐

Turn ....

Forward ☐

Turn .... to house ☐

Jimmy's route

Forward ☐

Turn ....

Forward ☐

Turn .... to house ☐

b. Write the routes from home to the bus stop.

Karl lives at No. 10

Turn ....

Forward ☐

Turn ....

Forward ☐ to bus stop.

Leone lives at No. 4

Turn ....

Forward ☐

Turn ....

Forward ☐ to bus stop.

2 This is the route the yacht took to the finish. Write the route.

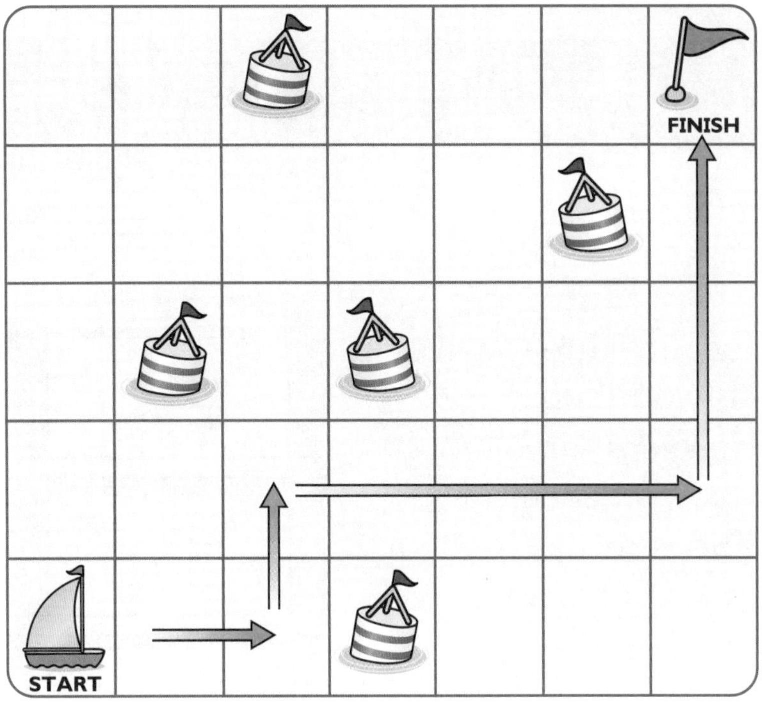

Forward [2]

Turn left

Forward [ ]

Turn ....

Forward [ ]

Turn ....

Forward [ ]

3 Draw two more routes in the above picture with coloured pens. Write them down.

a. Forward [ ]

Turn ....

Forward [ ]

Turn ....

Forward [ ]

Turn ....

Forward [ ]

b. Forward [ ]

Turn ....

Forward [ ]

Turn ....

Forward [ ]

Turn ....

Forward [ ]

I can give and follow instructions to move along a route. [ ]

Let's try this!

Get a partner to do this activity. Put a coin on the yacht.
Choose a route from Question 3. Read it out aloud.
Tell your partner to move the coin.
Now your partner takes their turn to read out the route.

9.5 In position

- I can describe and mark a position on a grid.

Key words
position, grid, to the right, to the left, above, below, between, under

Joel has three shelves in his workshop.
He keeps three tool boxes on each shelf.
This is what's in them.

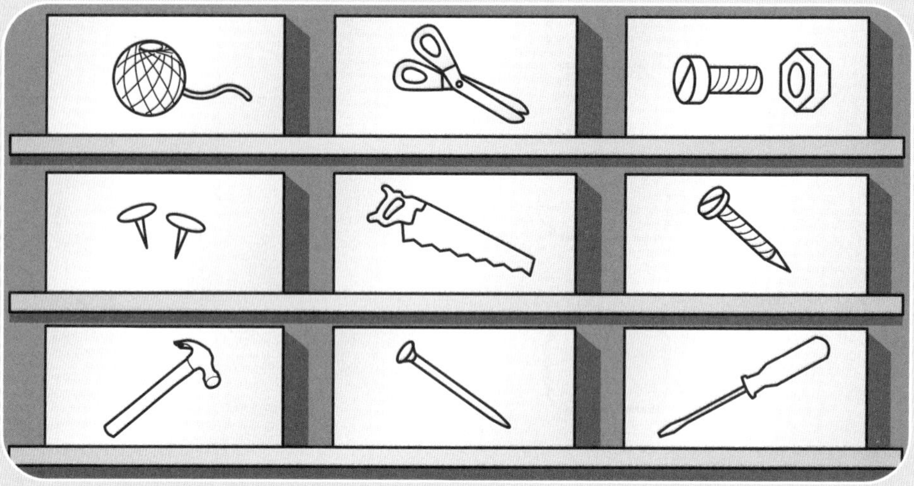

1 Draw what is:

a. on the right of the 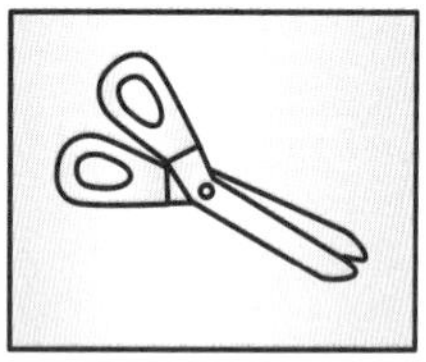

b. on the left of the 

c. on the right of the 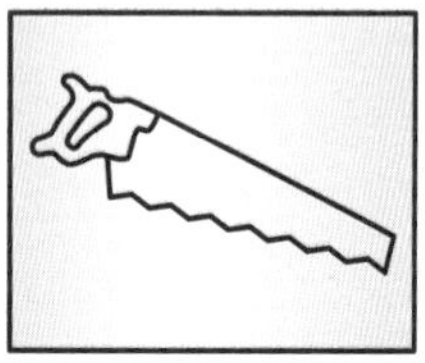

d. under the 

e. above the 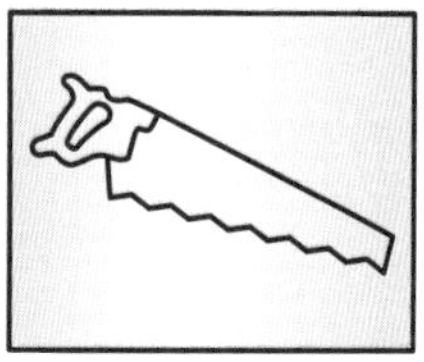

f. below the 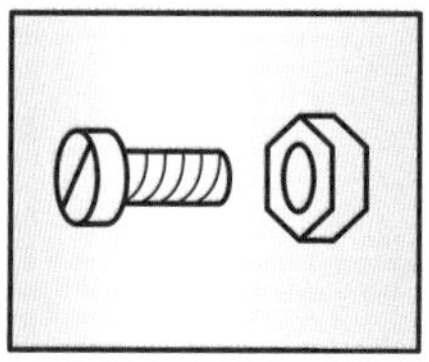

g. between the 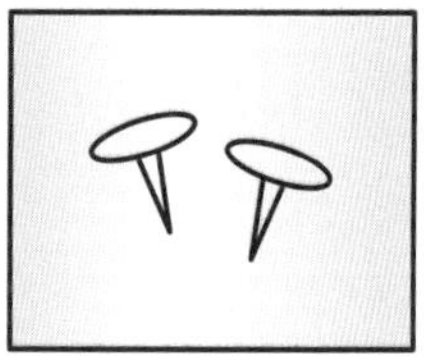 and the 

2 Draw each shape in its box.

		⬢		

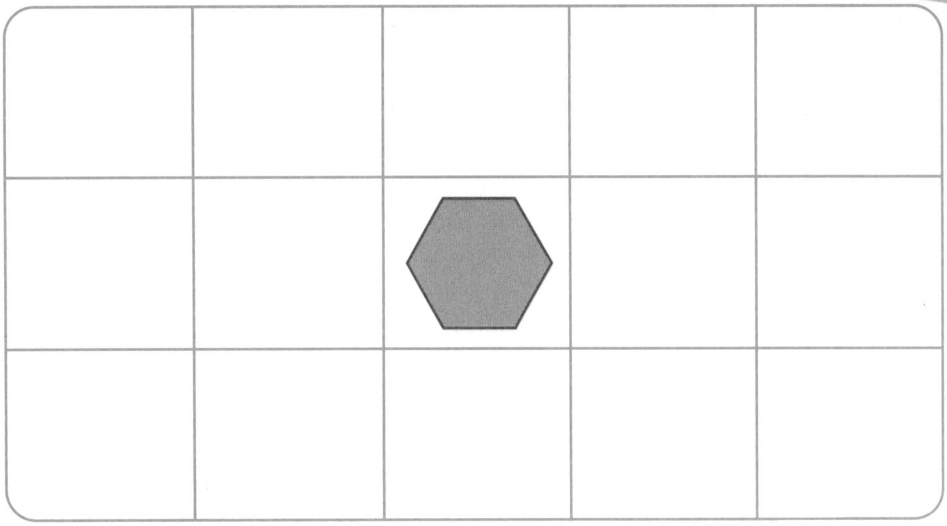

a. The ◯ is above the ⬢ .

b. The △ is two squares to the left of ◯ .

c. The □ is below the ⬢ .

d. The ▭ is two squares to the right of the □ .

e. The ⬠ is two squares above the ▭ .

f. Draw a ◠ between the △ and the ◯ .

g. Draw a ◺ two squares below the ◠ .

h. The square between □ and □ is empty.

◆ I can describe and mark a position on a grid. □

Let's try this!

- Draw each shape in a different box.

  △ ◯ ■ □ ⬠

- Write a sentence about the position of each shape in the grid.

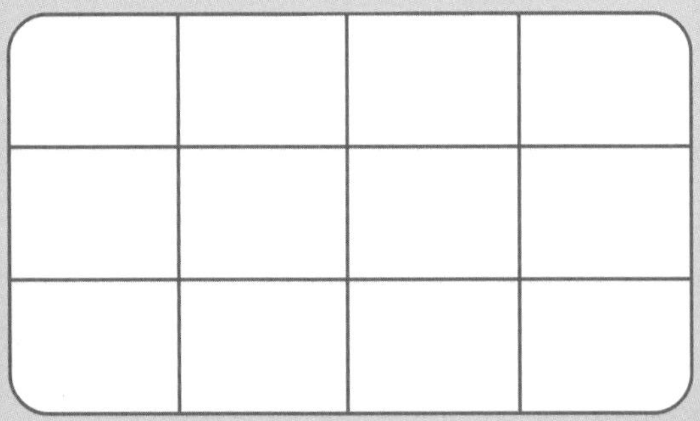

10.1 Market stall weights

- I can estimate, measure and compare weights in kg and $\frac{1}{2}$ kg.

Key words
kilogram (kg), estimate, measure, compare, weigh, about, lighter, heavier

1 You will need:

- 1 kilogram (kg) weight or 1 kg bag of sugar
- kitchen scales
- about $1\frac{1}{2}$ kg of each of these (or any objects in your classroom):
  - potatoes
  - apples
  - carrots
  - bananas

Get a 1 kg weight to feel how heavy it is.

Guess how many of each food weighs about 1 kg.

Use kitchen scales to measure and check your answer.

I'm using my hands to estimate how many oranges will weigh about 1 kg. Then I'll use the scales to check my guess of four oranges.
1kg

	How many in 1 kg	
Item	Estimate	Check
Oranges	about 4	4 ✓
Potatoes		
Apples		
Carrots		
Bananas		

2 Use your answers in Question 1 to fill in this table.

Item	How many in 1 kg	How many in 2 kg
Oranges	4	8
Potatoes		
Apples		
Carrots		
Bananas		

3 Use the words **lighter** or **heavier** to finish each sentence.

a. The apples are.............................than 1 kg.

b. The peaches are.............................than 1 kg.

c. The cherries are.............................than 1 kg.

d. The apples are.............................than the peaches.

e. The peaches are.............................than the cherries.

4 Write the weight of each box in kilograms.

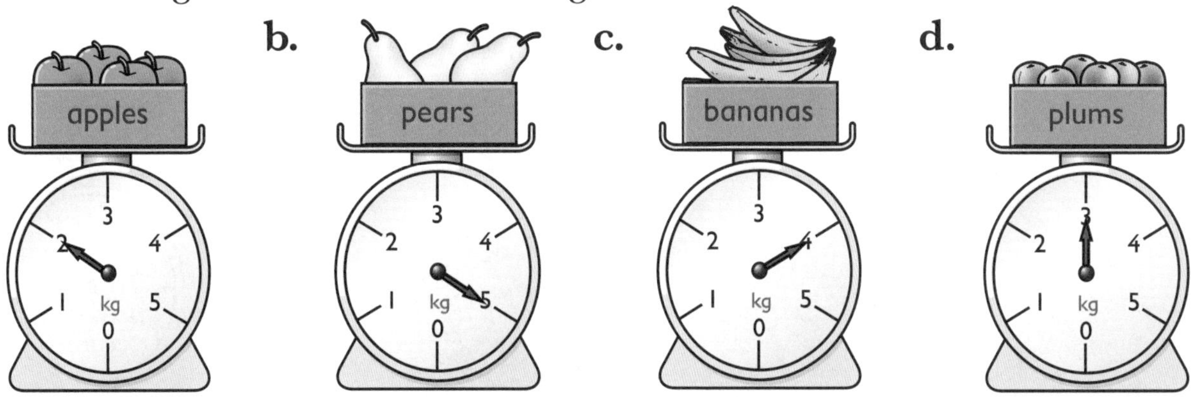

a. ☐ kg b. ☐ kg c. ☐ kg d. ☐ kg

I can estimate and compare weights in kg and $\frac{1}{2}$ kg. ☐

Let's try this!

Find the weight of one part if the water melon is cut into:

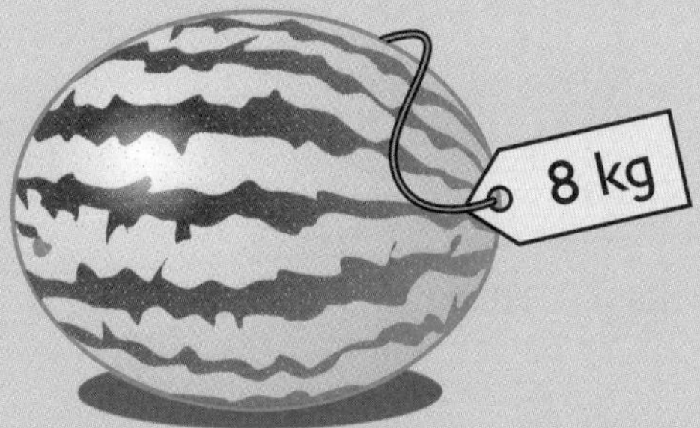

a. 2 equal parts. ☐ kg

b. 4 equal parts. ☐ kg

c. 8 equal parts. ☐ kg

10.2 Market scales

- I can read numbers on a scale to the nearest $\frac{1}{2}$ kg.

Key words
kilogram (kg), half kilogram ($\frac{1}{2}$ kg), weight, scales, about, nearly, just over, just under

This fish weighs just under 3 kilograms.
3
2
4
1
kg
5
0

1 Draw an arrow to show the weight of each fish.

a. This fish weighs about 3 kg.

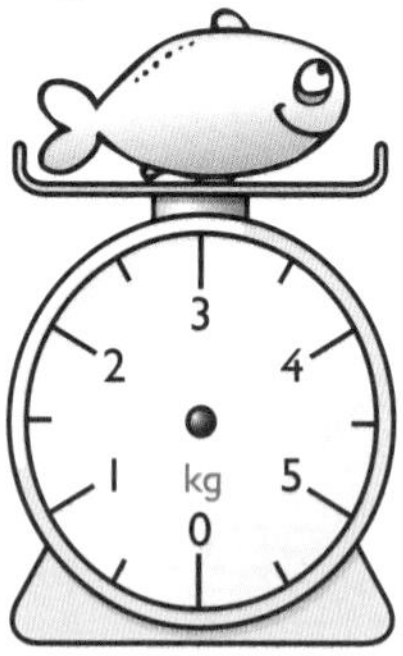

b. This fish weighs nearly 2 kg.

c. This fish weighs just under 5 kg.

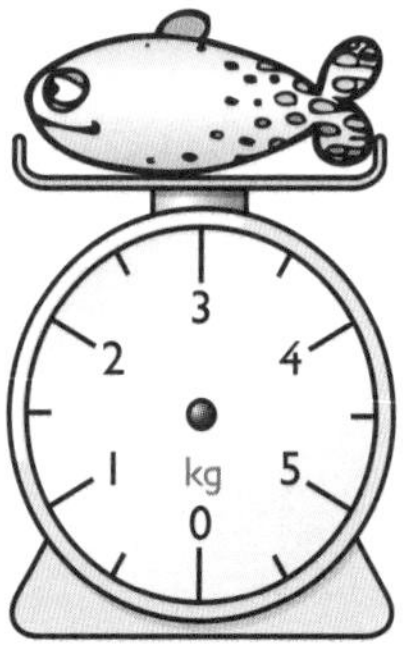

d. This fish weighs just over 4 kg.

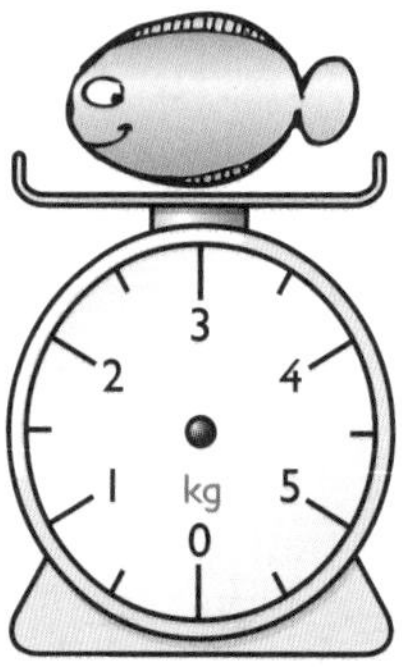

e. This fish weighs just under 1 kg.

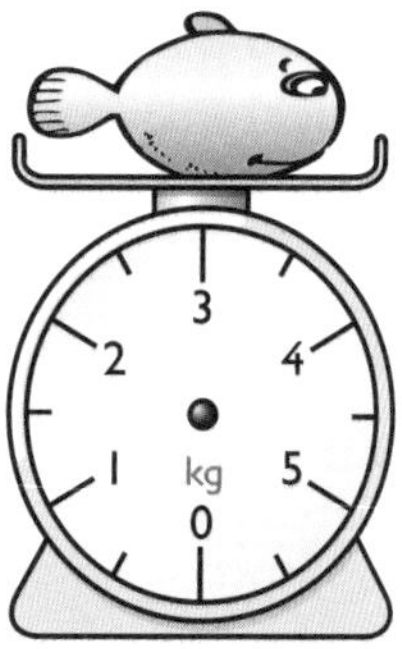

f. This fish weighs just over 5 kg

2 Write the weight of each vegetable box in kilograms.

a.

kg

b.

kg

c.

kg

3 Write the weight of each box of leeks to the nearest $\frac{1}{2}$ kg.

a.

kg

b.

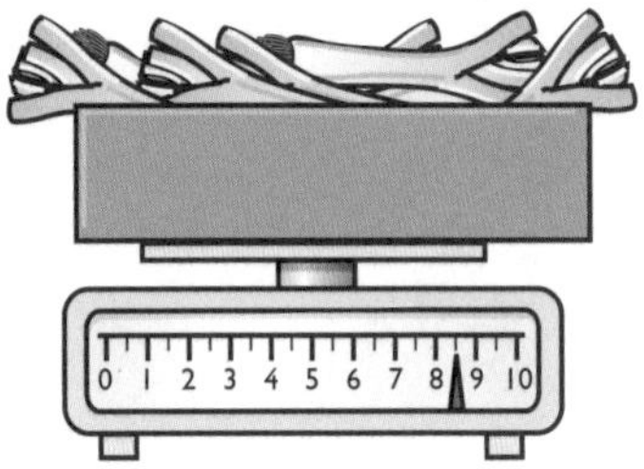

kg

c.

kg

d.

kg

e.

kg

f.

kg

◆ I can read numbers on a scale to the nearest $\frac{1}{2}$ kg.

Let's try this!

Look at your answers for Question 2. Write the weight of one box, then of two boxes and four boxes in the table.

Vegetable	1 box	2 boxes	4 boxes
Carrots	....5....kg	.........kg	.........kg
Onions	.........kg	.........kg	.........kg
Potatoes	.........kg	.........kg	.........kg

10.3 Calculating capacities

- I can compare capacities and work out capacities in litres.

Key words
capacity, compare, holds more, holds less, double, container, measuring jug, litre (l)

1 Look at the picture above.

a. Count the number of cups each container will fill. Write its letter on the measuring jug scale.

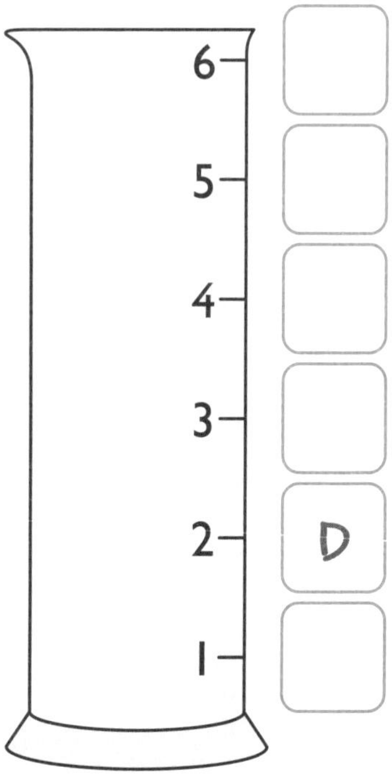

b. Use the words **holds more** or **holds less** to finish each sentence.

- C .... than A.
- B .... than D.

c. Complete these sentences.

- C holds double ☐ .
- ☐ + B hold the same as A.
- A + ☐ together hold the same as ☐ + C.

2 **a.** A full kettle holds ☐ litres of water.

b. If you fill the teapot with water from the kettle there will be ☐ litre of water left in the kettle.

c. The 2 litres teapot will make 10 cups of tea. Finish these sentences.

- 1 litres makes ☐ cups of tea.
- 3 litres makes ☐ cups of tea.
- 4 litres makes ☐ cups of tea.
- 5 litres makes ☐ cups of tea.

3 A DIY store sells tins of paint in these sizes.

Draw the tins of paint you will need to buy to get:

a. 3 litres of paint. **b.** 5 litres of paint. **c.** 6 litres of paint. **d.** 7 litres of paint.

a.	b.	c.	d.

◆ I can compare capacities and work out capacities in litres. ☐

Let's try this!

Paint is sold in 2 litre and 4 litre tins.
You need 10 litres of paint. Which and how many tins do you buy?
Can you find a different way?

10.4 Litres and half litres

- I can read scales marked in litres and $\frac{1}{2}$ litres.

Key words
capacity, container, measuring jug, litre (l), half litre ($\frac{1}{2}l$)

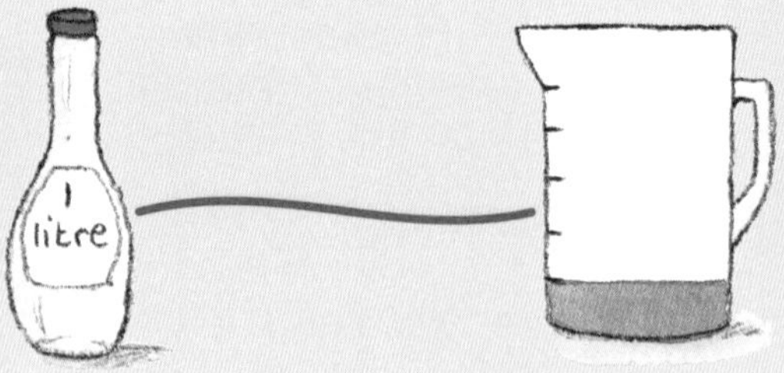

1 litre of olive oil in the bottle matches with 1 litre of oil in the measuring jug.

1 **a.** Match each container to its measuring jug.

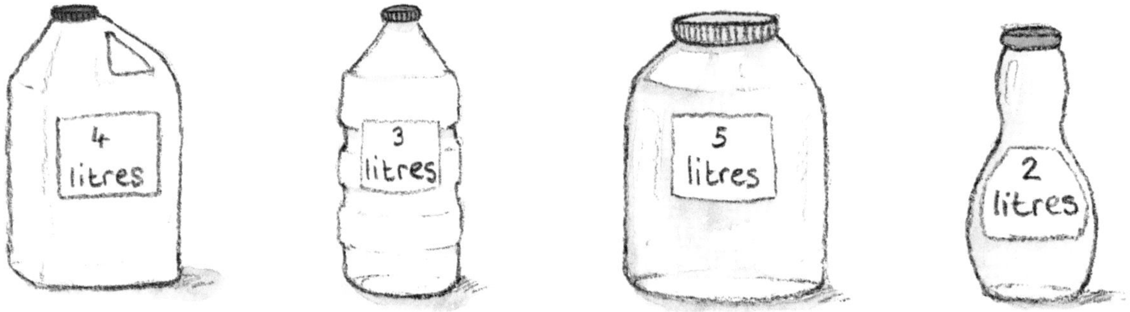

b. Draw a line to show how much water is in each jug.

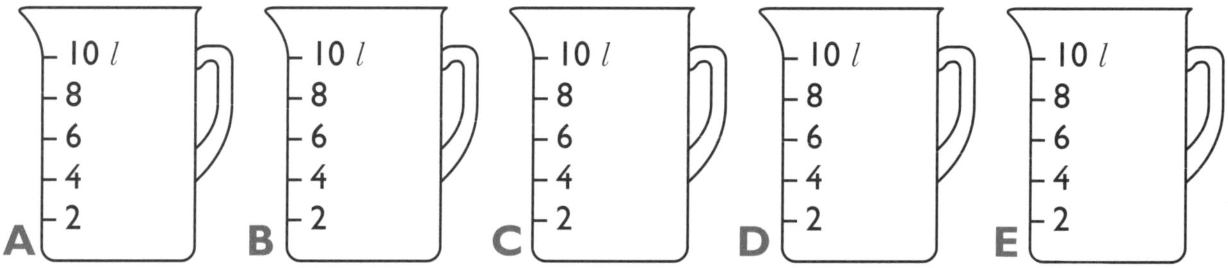

4 l 8 l 5 l 7 l 3 l

2 Write how much juice is in each jug to the nearest $\frac{1}{2}$ litre.

a. 

$2\frac{1}{2}$ *l*

b. 

☐ *l*

c. 

☐ *l*

d. 

☐ *l*

e. 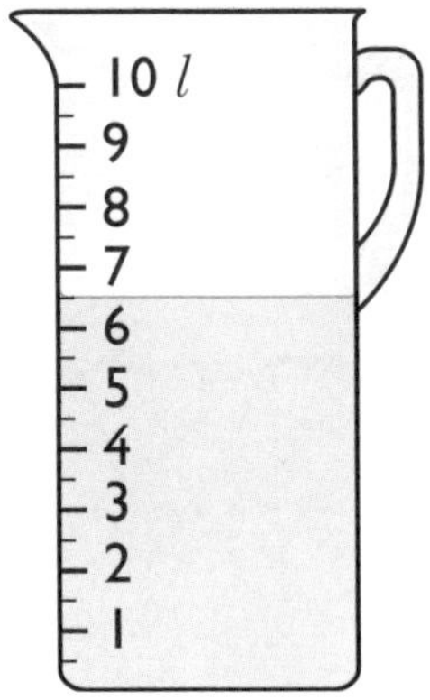

☐ *l*

f. 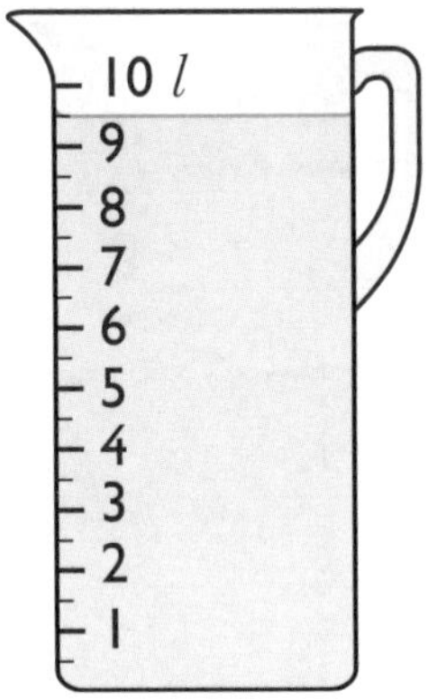

☐ *l*

g. 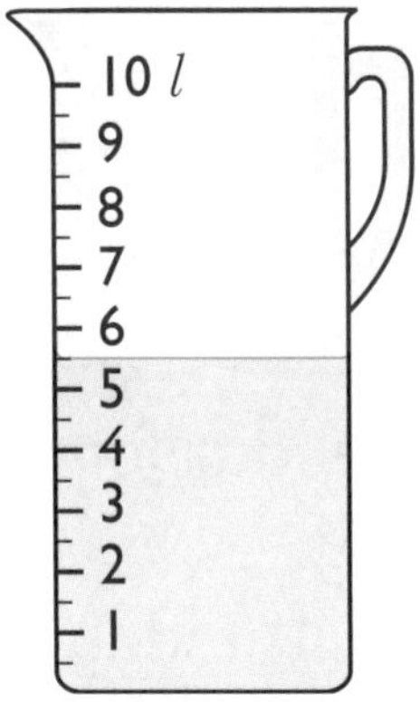

☐ *l*

h. 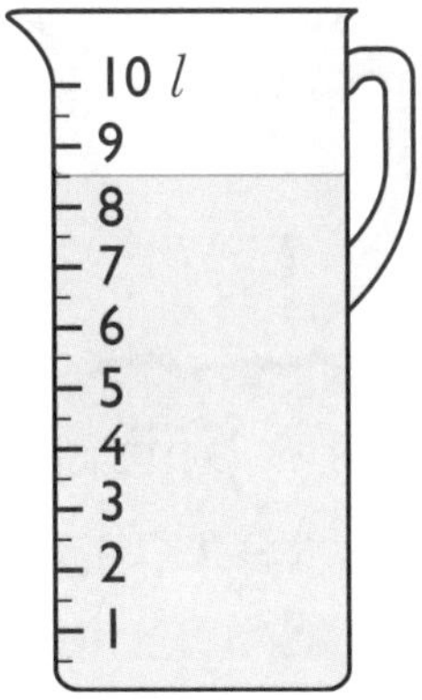

☐ *l*

3 Use colours to show how much milk and juice is there in each jug.
Write it under the jug.

a. Orange
2 *l* milk
$\frac{1}{2}$ *l* juice

☐ *l*

b. Lime
5 *l* milk
1 *l* juice

☐ *l*

c. Peach
$3\frac{1}{2}$ *l* milk
1 *l* juice

☐ *l*

◆ I can read scales marked in litres and $\frac{1}{2}$ litres. ☐

Let's try this!

Look at the jugs in Question 1a on page 100.
Find three different ways to make a total of 9 *l* with these jugs.

10.5 Days, weeks and months

- I can order days of the week and months of the year.

Key words
day, week, month, days of the week, months of the year

What is the 3rd day of the week?

Monday	Tuesday	Wednesday	Thursday	Friday	Saturday	Sunday
1	2	3	4	5	6	7

This is part of the calendar for June 2009.
The 1st day is Monday.
Monday comes before Tuesday.
Monday comes after Sunday.
The 3rd day of the week is Wednesday.

1 **a.** Write the days of the week in order from the 1st of June 2009.

1st ....

2nd ....

3rd Wednesday

4th ....

5th ....

6th ....

7th ....

b. Fill in these luggage labels.

FLIGHT TO PARIS
LEAVE 3 JUNE
DAY: Wednesday

FLIGHT TO ROME
LEAVE 3 JUNE
DAY: ....

FLIGHT TO NEW YORK
LEAVE [ ] JUNE
DAY: SUNDAY

FLIGHT TO CAPE TOWN
LEAVE [ ] JUNE
DAY: TUESDAY

2 These months are all mixed up.

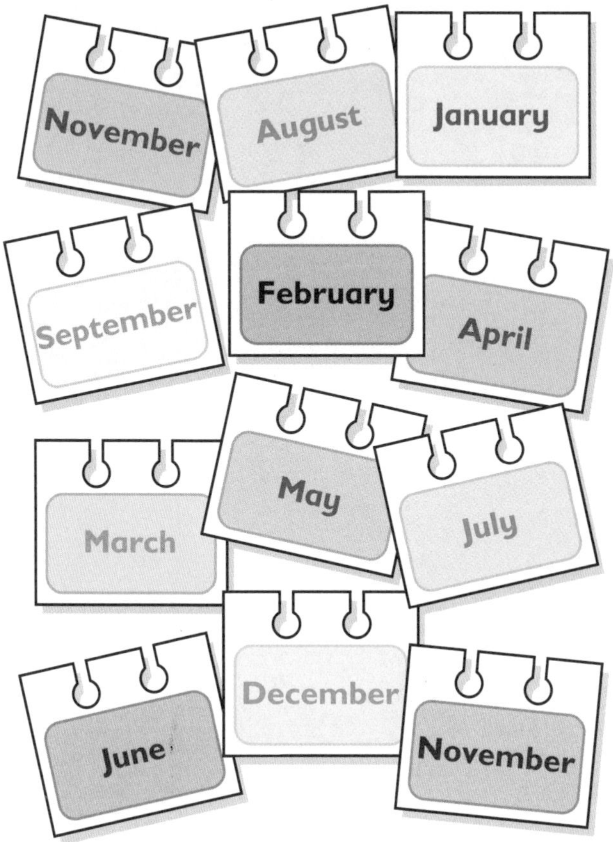

Write the months of the year in order.

1. January
2. ....
3. ....
4. ....
5. ....
6. June
7. ....
8. ....
9. ....
10. ....
11. ....
12. ....

3 Write **after** or **before** to complete these sentences.

a. June comes after May.

b. February comes .... January.

c. May comes .... April.

d. November comes .... December.

e. September comes .... August.

I can order days of the week and months of the year. ☐

Let's try this!

Use your list of months from Question 2.
When are your friends' birthdays?
Write them next to the months.

William Collins' dream of knowledge for all began with the publication of his first book in 1819. A self-educated mill worker, he not only enriched millions of lives, but also founded a flourishing publishing house. Today, staying true to this spirit, Collins books are packed with inspiration, innovation and practical expertise. They place you at the centre of a world of possibility and give you exactly what you need to explore it.

Collins. Freedom to teach.

Published by Collins
An imprint of HarperCollinsPublishers
77-85 Fulham Palace Road
Hammersmith
London
W6 8JB

10 9 8 7 6 5 4 3 2 1

ISBN-13 978-0-00-730285-7

British Library Cataloguing in Publication Data
A Catalogue record for this publication is available from the British Library.

Commissioned by Priya Govindan
Edited by Juliet Smith
Literacy reviewer Cliff Moon
Proofread by Lynn Watkins
Design and typesetting by Mark Walker and Steve Evans Design
Covers by Julie Martin
Illustrations by Mark Walker and Steve Evans
Printed and bound by Martins the Printers, Berwick-upon-Tweed
Production by Therese Theron

Answers

Chapter 1 Understanding Number

1.1 Counting

1 **a.** to **h.** Answers may vary.

2 **a.** 24 **b.** 17 **c.** 45 **d.** 38 **e.** 29 **f.** 42

3 Numbers 1 to 50 written in the grid.

Let's try this!

Answers may vary.

1.2 Place value

1 **a.** 14 **b.** 15 **c.** 18 **d.** 19 **e.** 16 **f.** 11 **g.** 13 **i.** 20 **j.** 10 **k.** 12

2 **a.** Two blocks of ten, three blocks of one (20 and 3)
b. Two blocks of ten, eight blocks of one (20 and 8)
c. Three blocks of ten, six blocks of one (30 and 6)
d. Three blocks of ten, one block of one (30 and 1)

Let's try this!

45, 17, 32, and others

1.3 Ordering numbers

1 **a.** to **f.** Answers may vary.

2 **a.** to **f.** Answers may vary.

3 **a.** 4, 6, 15, 17, 28 **b.** 2, 12, 20, 28, 32
c. 12, 19, 23, 36, 48 **d.** 3, 13, 30, 37, 43
e. 10, 14, 40, 41, 44 **f.** 11, 15, 25, 35, 50

Let's try this!

Answers may vary.

1.4 One more, one less

1 **a.** 17 **b.** 24 **c.** 39 **d.** 13 **e.** 44 **f.** 16 **g.** 48 **h.** 32

2 **a.** 14 **b.** 33 **c.** 22 **d.** 47 **e.** 20 **f.** 29 **g.** 50 **h.** 37 **i.** 24

3 **a.** 17 **b.** 19 **c.** 36 **d.** 15 **e.** 47 **f.** 48 **g.** 32 **h.** 24

4 **a.** 17 **b.** 36 **c.** 25 **d.** 40 **e.** 23 **f.** 32 **g.** 47 **h.** 44 **i.** 28

Let's try this!

a. Numbers that are two more: 14, 38, 43, 31, 10, 32, 46, 52
b. Numbers that are two less: 10, 34, 39, 27, 6, 28, 42, 48

1.5 10 more, 10 less

1 **a.** 24 **b.** 31 **c.** 39 **d.** 20 **e.** 56 **f.** 23 **g.** 45 **h.** 52

2 **a.** 26 **b.** 45 **c.** 34 **d.** 54 **e.** 32 **f.** 41

3 **a.** 7 **b.** 18 **c.** 30 **d.** 29 **e.** 1 **f.** 35 **g.** 13 **h.** 9

4 **a.** 9 **b.** 23 **c.** 11 **d.** 27 **e.** 19 **f.** 25 **g.** 34 **h.** 31 **i.** 18

Let's try this!

Answers may vary.

Chapter 2 Addition

2.1 Understanding addition

1 **a.** to **l.** Answers may vary.

2 **a.** 6 + 5 = 11 **b.** 4 + 7 =11 **c.** 2 + 8 =10
d. 9 + 3 =12 **e.** 2 + 6 = 8 **f.** 1 + 8 = 9
g. 4 + 3 + 7 **h.** 7 + 2 = 9 **i.** 5 + 5 = 10

Let's try this!

Answers may vary.

2.2 Adding with a number line (1)

1 **a.** 9 **b.** 15 **c.** 11 **d.** 11 **e.** 14 **f.** 17 **g.** 18 **h.** 15 **i.** 20 **j.** 17 **k.** 18 **l.** 19

2 **a.** 19 **b.** 16 **c.** 18 **d.** 19 **e.** 19 **f.** 19 **g.** 19 **h.** 18 **i.** 15 **j.** 17 **k.** 17 **l.** 17

3 There will be lesser number of jumps to count on.

Let's try this!

Answers may vary.

2.3 Adding with a number line (2)

1 **a.** 31 **b.** 33 **c.** 29 **d.** 34 **e.** 32 **f.** 37 **g.** 37 **h.** 34 **i.** 38 **j.** 37 **k.** 40 **l.** 37

2 **a.** 24 +7 = 31 **b.** 8 + 21 = 29 **c.** 7 + 33 = 40
d. 9 + 26 = 35 **e.** 28 + 8 = 36 **f.** 11 + 24 = 35
g. 30 + 8 = 38 **h.** 14 + 21 = 35 **i.** 29 + 7 = 36

Let's try this!

a. 19 **b.** 21 **c.** 24 **d.** 25 **e.** 23 **f.** 28

2.4 Addition facts for 10

1 **a.** 5 **b.** 8 **c.** 3 **d.** 1 **e.** 6 **f.** 10

2 **a.** 6 + 3 **b.** 5 + 4 **c.** 3 + 6 **d.** 2 + 7 **e.** 1 + 8 **f.** 9 + 0

3 **a.** 7 **b.** 5 **c.** 7 **d.** 8 **e.** 10 **f.** 6 **g.** 9 **h.** 10 **i.** 7 **j.** 9 **k.** 9 **l.** 10

4 **a.** Double 2 is 4; 2 + 2 = 4
b. Double 5 is 10; 5 + 5 = 10
c. Double 1 is 2; 1 + 1 = 2
d. Double 3 is 6; 3 + 3 = 6
e. Double 4 is 8; 4 + 4 = 8
f. Double 0 is 0; 0 + 0 = 0

Let's try this!

Answers may vary.

2.5 Addition facts for 20

1 **a.** 13 + 7 = 20 **b.** 10 + 10 = 20 **c.** 18 + 2 = 20
d. 11 + 9 = 20 **e.** 16 + 4 = 20 **f.** 19 + 1 = 20
g. 14 + 6 = 20 **h.** 8 + 12 = 20 **i.** 6 + 14 = 20

2 **a.** 7 **b.** 18 **c.** 12 **d.** 9 **e.** 5
f. 1 **g.** 17 **h.** 4 **i.** 14 **j.** 10
k. 7 **l.** 20

Let's try this!
Answers may vary.

Chapter 3 Subtraction

3.1 Understanding subtraction

1 Answers may vary.

2 **a.** 6 **b.** 7 **c.** 2 **d.** 7 **e.** 6
f. 4 **g.** 9 **h.** 3 **i.** 6 **j.** 8
k. 5 **l.** 5 **m.** 4 **n.** 1 **o.** 10

Let's try this!
Answers may vary.

3.2 Subtracting with a number line (1)

1 **a.** 8 **b.** 6 **c.** 7 **d.** 6 **e.** 4
f. 7 **g.** 0 **h.** 4 **i.** 13 **j.** 12
k. 11 **l.** 10

2 **a.** ✓8 **b.** ✓5 **c.** ✓7 **d.** ✗ **e.** ✓4
f. ✗ **g.** ✓11 **h.** ✓7 **i.** ✗

3 You have to take away the smallest number from the biggest number.

Let's try this!
Answers may vary.

Lesson 3.3 Subtracting with a number line (2)

1 **a.** 31 **b.** 24 **c.** 28 **d.** 24 **e.** 23
f. 27 **g.** 35 **h.** 31 **i.** 22 **j.** 26
k. 29 **l.** 20

2 **a.** 29 – 6 = 23 **b.** 27 – 5 = 22 **c.** 33 – 4 = 29
d. 31 – 8 = 23 **e.** 27 – 3 = 24 **f.** 34 – 11 = 23
g. 40 – 7 = 33 **h.** 31 – 10 = 21 **i.** 39 – 6 = 33
j. 34 – 3 = 31 **k.** 32 – 5 = 27 **l.** 37 – 9 = 28

Let's try this!
Answers may vary.

3.4 Subtraction facts to 10

1 **a.** 5 **b.** 7 **c.** 0 **d.** 9 **e.** 1
f. 4 **g.** 8 **h.** 3 **i.** 6 **j.** 2
k. 3 **l.** 10

2 **a.** 5 – 2 **b.** 5 – 1 **c.** 5 – 3 **d.** 5 – 4
e. 5 – 5 **f.** 5 – 0

3 **a.** 5 **b.** 7 **c.** 3 **d.** 4 **e.** 4
f. 7 **g.** 3 **h.** 0 **i.** 1 **j.** 4
k. 1 **l.** 2

Let's try this!
Answers may vary.

3.5 Subtraction facts for 20

1 **a.** 20 – 3 = 17 **b.** 20 – 9 = 11 **c.** 20 – 5 = 1
d. 20 – 1 = 19 **e.** 20 – 7 = 13 **f.** 20 – 10 = 10
g. 20 – 6 = 14 **h.** 20 – 15 = 5 **i.** 20 – 2 = 18

2 **a.** 20 – 13 = 7, 20 – 7 = 13
b. 20 – 8 = 12, 20 – 12 = 8
c. 20 – 11 = 9, 20 – 9 = 11
d. 20 – 15 = 5, 20 – 5 = 15
e. 20 – 19 = 1, 20 – 1 = 19
f. 20 – 3 = 17, 20 – 17 = 3
g. 20 – 16 = 4, 20 – 4 = 16
h. 20 – 6 = 14, 20 – 14 = 6
i. 20 – 10 = 10, 20 – 10 = 10
j. 20 – 0 = 20, 20 – 20 = 0

Let's try this!
Answers may vary.

Chapter 4 Fractions

4.1 Understanding fractions

1 **a.** ✓ **b.** ✗ **c.** ✓ **d.** ✗ **e.** ✗
f. ✗ **g.** ✓ **h.** ✓ **i.** ✗

2 **a.** to **j.** The line should show two equal parts.

3 The line should show two equal parts.

Let's try this!
The two parts must be equal.

4.2 Halves of numbers

1 **a.** 3 **b.** 2 **c.** 4 **d.** 1 **e.** 7
f. 8 **g.** 6 **h.** 10

2 **a.** 2 each **b.** 5 each **c.** 9 each
d. 6 each **e.** 4 each **f.** 8 each

3 **a.** 6 chocolates **b.** 4 chocolates **c.** 5 chocolates
d. 10 chocolates **e.** 8 chocolates

Let's try this!
Answers may vary.

4.3 Quarters of shapes

1 **a.** ✗ **b.** ✓ **c.** ✓ **d.** ✗ **e.** ✓
f. ✗ **g.** ✓ **h.** ✓ **i.** ✗

2 **a.** to **j.** The lines should show four equal parts.

Let's try this!
Answers may vary.

4.4 Quarters of numbers

1 **a.** 2 **b.** 1 **c.** 4
d. 5 **e.** 3 **f.** 6

2 **a.** 1 each **b.** 3 each **c.** 5 each
d. 2 each **e.** 4 each **f.** A quarter

3 **a.** 2 dots drawn in blank quarter
b. 5 dots drawn in blank quarter
c. 1 dot drawn in blank quarter
d. 3 dots drawn in blank quarter
e. 4 dots drawn in blank quarter
f. 6 dots drawn in blank quarter

Let's try this!
Numbers that make quarters:
4, 8, 12, 16, 20, 24, 28, 32…

Lesson 4.5 Halves and quarters

1 **a.** $\frac{1}{2}$ **b.** $\frac{1}{2}$ **c.** $\frac{1}{2}$ **d.** $\frac{1}{4}$ **e.** $\frac{1}{4}$
f. $\frac{1}{2}$ **g.** $\frac{1}{4}$ **h.** $\frac{1}{4}$ **i.** $\frac{1}{2}$

2 **a.** **b.** **c.** **d.**

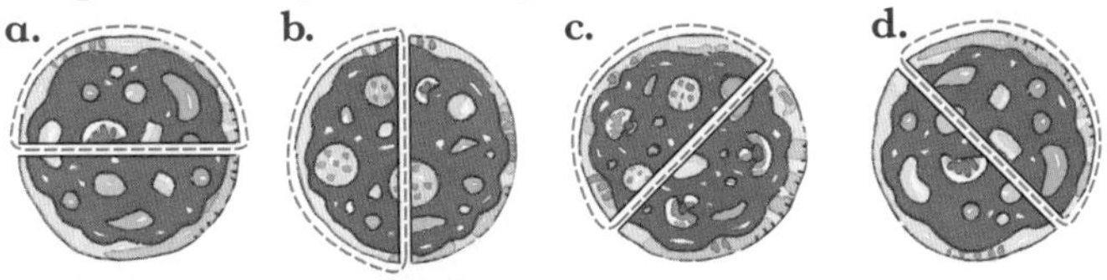

3 **a.** **b.**

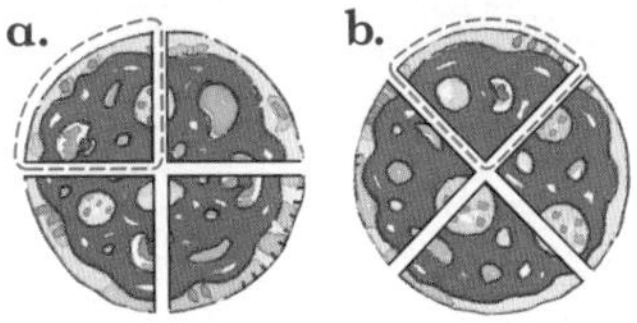

4 **a.** **b.** **c.** **d.** **e.** **f.**

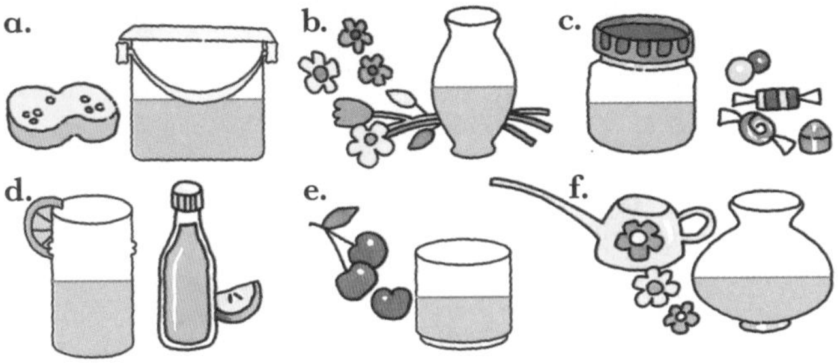

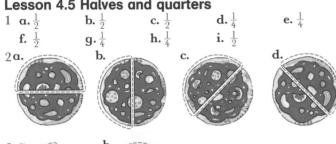

Let's try this!
One apple and a half apples each.

Chapter 5
Measure – Length and Time

5.1 Measuring in metres

1 Answers may vary.
2 Answers may vary.
3 **a.** 7 m **b.** 4 m **c.** 9 m **d.** 6 m

Let's try this!
Answers may vary.

5.2 Measuring in centimetres

1 **a.**

Colour	Estimate	Measure
Red		5 cm
Green		9 cm
Yellow		7 cm
Orange		11 cm
Pink		4 cm
Blue		10 cm

b. The shortest string is **4** cm long.
c. The longest string is **11** cm long.
d. The yellow ribbon is **3** cm shorter than the blue ribbon.
e. The orange ribbon is **7** cm longer than the pink ribbon.

2

Green line	a	b	c	d	e
Length in cm	4 cm	7 cm	13 cm	11 cm	14 cm

3 **a.** 4 cm + 5 cm = 9 cm **b.** 7 cm + 4 cm = 11 cm
c. 11 cm + 3 cm = 14 cm **d.** 13 cm – 4 cm = 9 cm
e. 14 cm – 5 cm = 9 cm

Let's try this!
Answers may vary.

5.3 How long is it?

1 Answers may vary.
2 **a.** A to B = 13 cm **b.** C to D = 9 cm
c. D to E = 12 cm **d.** E to A = 15 cm
e. C to B = 10 cm
f. C to D, C to B, D to E, A to B, E to A
g. The lines join up to make a star.

Let's try this!
Answers may vary.

5.4 Time clocks

1 **a.** 10 o'clock **b.** 5 o'clock **c.** $\frac{1}{2}$ past 11 **d.** $\frac{1}{2}$ past 3

2 **a.** **b.** **c.** **d.** **e.** **f.**

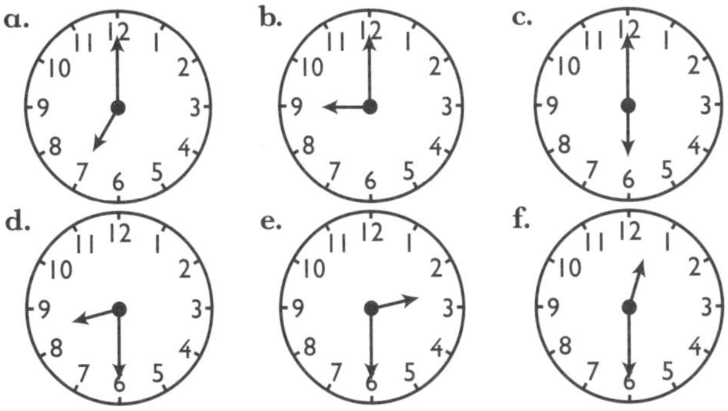

3 **a.** $\frac{1}{2}$ past 6 **b.** 8 o'clock **c.** $\frac{1}{2}$ past 10 **d.** 9 o'clock

Let's try this!
$\frac{1}{2}$ past 4

5.5 Digital times

1 **a.** 9 o'clock **b.** 4 o'clock **c.** 12 o'clock
d. $\frac{1}{2}$ past 2, two thirty **e.** $\frac{1}{2}$ past 11, eleven thirty
f. $\frac{1}{2}$ past 8, eight thirty **g.** 5 o'clock
h. $\frac{1}{2}$ past 6, six thirty **i.** $\frac{1}{2}$ past 7, seven thirty
2 **a.** 9:30 **b.** 11:00 **c.** 1:30 **d.** 12:00
3 Florida, 4:00 Spain, 7:30 Italy, 11:00 Greece, 10:30

Let's try this!
Yes, she is right. You can make 7:
1:00, 1:30, 2:00, 2:30, 3:00, 10:30, 12:30

Chapter 6
Understanding Shapes

6.1 Common 2-D shapes

1 **a.** Triangle **b.** Square **c.** Rectangle
d. Triangle **e.** Circle **f.** Rectangle

2 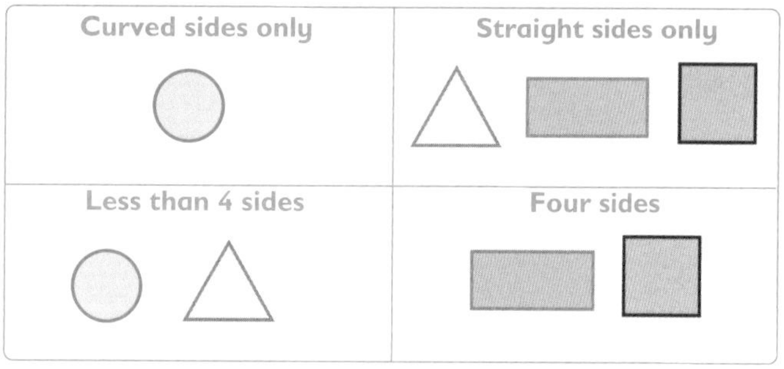

3 **Four** triangles in blue.
Two rectangles and **two** squares in red.
Two circles in yellow.
Two semi-circles in green.

Let's try this!
Alike – both shapes have four straight sides
Different – square: all sides are of the same length; rectangle: two short and two long sides

6.2 Pinboard shapes
1 **a.** to **c.** Answers may vary.
2 Answers may vary.
3 **a.** 6 sides **b.** 6 sides **c.** 5 sides **d.** 5 sides
e. 4 sides **f.** 5 sides **g.** 6 sides **h.** 5 sides

Let's try this!
Answers may vary.

6.3 Sides and corners
1 **a.** square: 4 sides, 4 corners
b. triangle: 3 sides, 3 corners
c. rectangle: 4 sides, 4 corners
d. hexagon: 6 sides, 6 corners
e. circle: 1 side, 0 corners
f. pentagon: 5 sides, 5 corners
g. triangle: 3 sides, 3 corners
h. semi-circle: 2 sides, 2 corners
i. pentagon: 5 sides, 5 corners
j. hexagon: 6 sides, 6 corners
3 **a.** 4 corners **b.** 4 corners **c.** 6 corners
d. 8 corners **e.** 8 corners **f.** 4 corners

Let's try this!
Answers may vary.

6.4 Common 3-D solids
1

Picture	Solid
1	Cube
2	Cone
3	Sphere
4	Cuboid
5	Cylinder

Picture	Solid
6	Cone
7	Sphere
8	Cylinder
9	Cuboid
10	Cube

2 **a.**

Curved face only	Flat faces only	Curved and flat faces
Sphere	Cube, cuboid	Cone, cylinder

b.

Corners	No corners
Cube, cuboid	Sphere, cone, cylinder

3 Answers will vary depending on what objects are used.

Rolls	Slides
Sphere, cylinder, cone (if rolling on the side)	Cube, cuboid, cone (if sliding on the flat surface)

Let's try this!
a. A cube has six square faces and eight corners.
b. A cuboid has six rectangular faces and eight corners.
c. A cylinder is shaped like a tin of (beans). Its ends are flat circles.

6.5 Building solids
1 Open
2

Cuboid	a.	b.	c.	d.	e.	f.
Number of red squares faces	10	4	5	10	9	8
Number of blue square faces	4	10	9	8	9	8

3

Shape	Number of square faces		
	Blue	Red	Yellow
a.	5	5	4
b.	5	4	5
c.	4	5	5
d.	5	5	4

4

Shape	Number of square faces				Total
	Blue	Red	Yellow	Green	
a.	5	5	4	4	18
b.	5	3	5	5	18
c.	5	4	4	5	18
d.	4	4	4	4	16

Let's try this!
Blue: 5 Red: 5 Yellow: 4 Green: 4

Chapter 7
Multiplication and Division

7.1 Counting in twos and tens
1 **a.** 2, 4, 6, 8, 10
b. 2, 4, 6
c. 2, 4, 6, 8, 10, 12, 14, 16
d. 2, 4, 6, 8
e. 2, 4, 6, 8, 10, 12, 14
f. 2, 4, 6, 8, 10, 12, 14, 16, 18
g. 2, 4, 6, 8, 10, 12
h. 2, 4, 6, 8, 10, 12, 14, 16, 18, 20

2 **a.** 10, 20, 30
b. 10, 20, 30, 40, 50
c. 10, 20
d. 10, 20, 30, 40, 50, 60
e. 10, 20, 30, 40
f. 10, 20, 30, 40, 50, 60, 70
g. 10, 20, 30, 40, 50, 60, 70, 80
h. 10, 20, 30, 40, 50, 60, 70, 80, 90, 100

3 2, 4, 6, 8, 10, 12, 14, 16, 18, 20

4 10, 20, 30, 40, 50, 60, 70, 80, 90, 100

Let's try this!
They all end in '0'.

7.2 Doubling and halving

1 **a.** Half of 6 is 3 **b.** Half of 2 is 1
c. Half of 10 is 5 **d.** Half of 4 is 2
e. Half of 12 is 6 **f.** Half of 8 is 4

2 **a.** 1, 1. Half of 2 is 1
b. 4, 4. Half of 8 is 4
c. 3, 3. Half of 6 is 3
d. 7, 7. Half of 14 is 7
e. 2, 2. Half of 4 is 2
f. 5, 5. Half of 10 is 5

3 **a.** Double 5 is 10 **b.** Double 3 is 6
c. Double 6 is 12 **d.** Double 7 is 14
e. Double 10 is 20 **f.** Double 1 is 2

Let's try this!
Half of 12 = 6 Half of 14 = 7
Half of 16 = 8 Half of 18 = 9

7.3 Understanding multiplication

1 **a.** 5 groups of 2 **b.** 3 groups of 2
c. 8 groups of 2 **d.** 6 groups of 2
e. 9 groups of 2 **f.** 7 groups of 2

2 **a.** 3 groups of 5 = 15 **b.** 2 groups of 4 = 8
c. 4 groups of 3 = 12 **d.** 2 groups of 10 = 20
e. 5 groups of 2 = 10 **f.** 4 groups of 5 = 20
g. 3 groups of 3 = 9 **h.** 2 groups of 6 = 12
i. 3 groups of 4 = 12 **j.** 6 groups of 3 = 18
k. Answers will vary.

Let's try this!
Groups of 2 Groups of 5
Groups of 4 Groups of 10

7.4 Multiplication as repeated addition

1 **a.** 4 + 4 = 8 **b.** 5 + 5 + 5 = 15
c. 6 + 6 = 12 **d.** 3 + 3 + 3 + 3 + 3 = 15
e. 4 + 4 + 4 + 4 = 16 **f.** 2 + 2 + 2 = 6
g. 4 + 4 + 4 = 12 **h.** 5 + 5 + 5 + 5 = 20
i. 10 + 10 + 10 = 30

2 **a.** 2 groups of 4 **b.** 3 groups of 5 **c.** 2 groups of 6
d. 5 groups of 3 **e.** 4 groups of 4 **f.** 3 groups of 2
g. 3 groups of 4 **h.** 4 groups of 5 **i.** 3 groups of 10

3 **a.** Draw 3 groups of 3 = 9
b. Draw 3 groups of 5 = 15
c. Draw 4 groups of 4 = 16
d. Draw 6 groups of 2 = 12
e. Draw 2 groups of 6 = 12
f. Draw 4 groups of 5 = 20
g. Draw 6 groups of 4 = 24
h. Draw 5 groups of 3 = 15

Let's try this!
5 + 5 + 5 = 15
3 + 3 + 3 + 3 + 3 = 15
3 groups of 5 is the same as 5 groups of 3.

7.5 Understanding division

1 **a.** 5 each **b.** 4 each **c.** 3 each **d.** 4 each
e. 7 each **f.** 3 each **g.** 3 each

2 **a.** No **b.** Yes **c.** No **d.** No **e.** Yes
f. Yes **g.** No **h.** No **i.** Yes **j.** Yes

Let's try this!
Cut one apple in half. They get one and a half apples each.

Chapter 8 Handling Data

8.1 Shopping lists

1 **a.** to **e.** Answers will vary.

2 **a.** 3 apples, 4 bananas, 2 pears, 6 mushrooms and 4 carrots
b. The 3rd item on the list is 2 pears.
There are 9 fruits. There are 10 vegetables.

Let's try this!

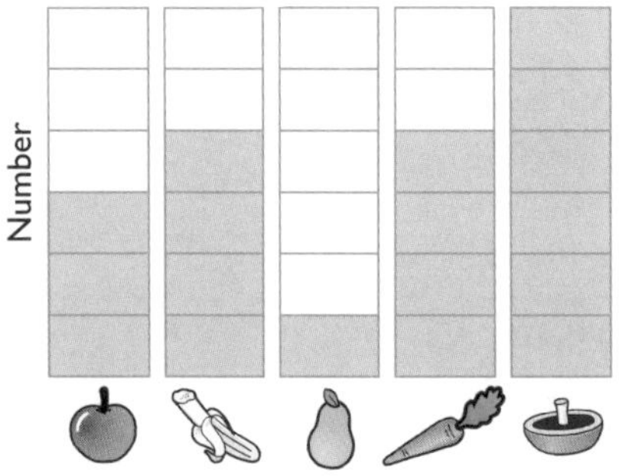

There are **2** more mushrooms than bananas.

8.2 Keeping a tally

1 **a.**

Tally	Numbers
IIII	4
卌 I	6
卌 III	8
卌 卌 II	12
卌 卌 卌 IIII	19
卌 卌 卌 卌	20

b.

Numbers	Tally
3	|||
7	卌 ||
10	卌 卌
13	卌 卌 |||
15	卌 卌 卌
18	卌 卌 卌 |||

2 Answers will vary.

3 **a.** and **b.** Answers will vary.

Let's try this!

Answers will vary.

8.3 Sorting diagrams for shapes

1

Shape	Number
Circle	5
Triangle	6
Square	9

2

	Orange	Not orange
Squares	✓✓ (2)	✓✓✓✓✓✓✓ (7)
Not squares	✓✓✓ (3)	✓✓✓✓✓✓✓✓ (8)

3

	3 sides	Not 3 sides
Blue	✓✓ (2)	✓✓✓ (3)
Not blue	✓✓✓✓ (4)	✓✓✓✓✓✓✓✓ ✓✓✓ (11)

4

3 sides	4 sides	5 sides	6 sides
b, h, i, o [4]	a, d, e, g, m [5]	f, j, n [3]	c, k, l [3]

Let's try this!

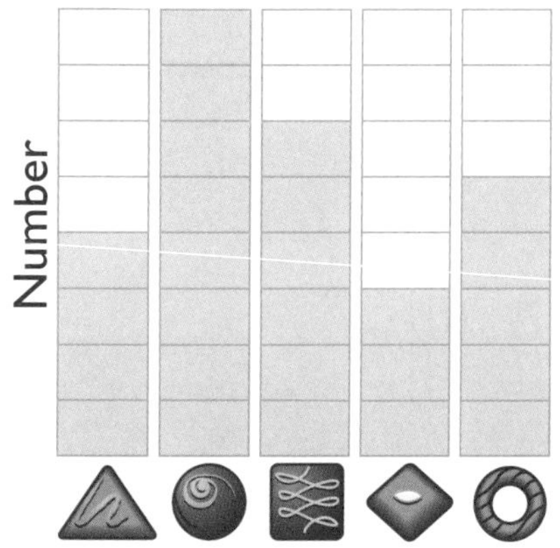

The least common shape is 

8.4 Using pictographs

1

Eggs

Small	○	○	○				
Medium	○	○	○	○			
Large	○	○	○	○	○		
Extra large	○	○	○	○			

Number of eggs

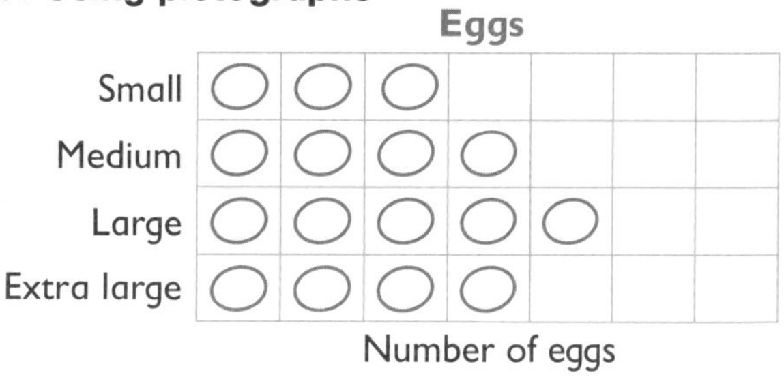

There are 2 more large size eggs than small size eggs.

2

Colour	Tally	Total
Black	|	1
Blue	卌 ||	7
Green	卌 |	6
Red	卌	5
Yellow	||||	4

3

Peter's game of pool

Black	○						
Blue	○	○	○	○	○	○	○
Green	○	○	○	○	○	○	
Red	○	○	○	○	○		
Yellow	○	○	○	○			

Number of balls potted

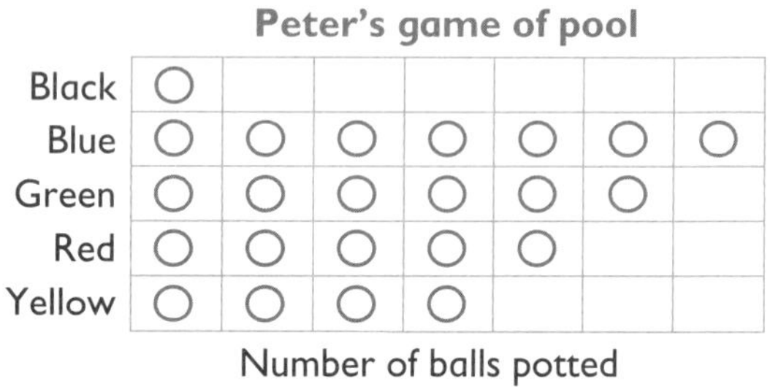

Let's try this!

Answers will vary.

8.5 Sorting coins

1 **a.** **4** 1p coins show tails. **b.** **1** 2p coin shows heads.

c. There are **8** copper coins altogether.

2 **a.**

	Heads	Tails
5p	✓✓ (2)	✓✓✓ (3)
10p	✓✓✓✓ (4)	✓✓ (2)

b. There are 5 silver coins that show heads.

c. There are 6 silver coins that show tails.

3 **a.**

Coins in Sandra's purse

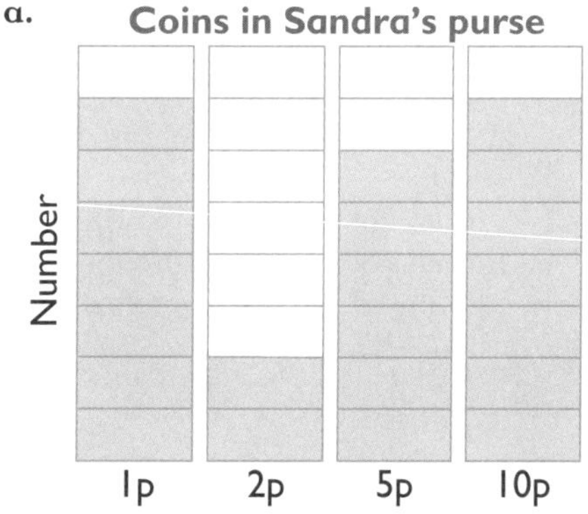

b. The least common coin is worth 2p.
c. Sandra has 10p in 1p and 2p coins.

Let's try this!

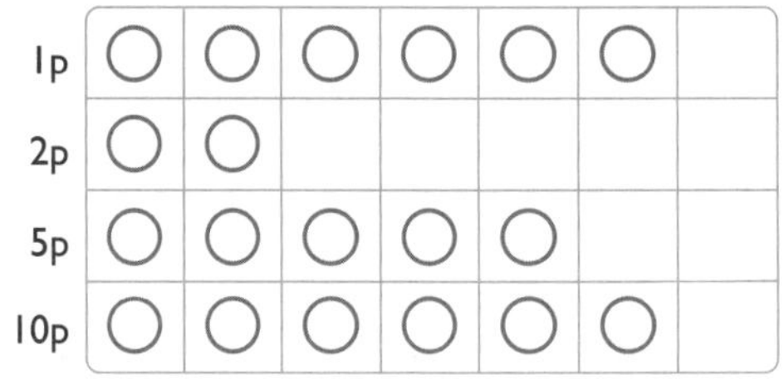

Sandra has **85p** in silver coins.

Chapter 9 More on Shapes

9.1 Draw a line of symmetry in 2-D shapes

1

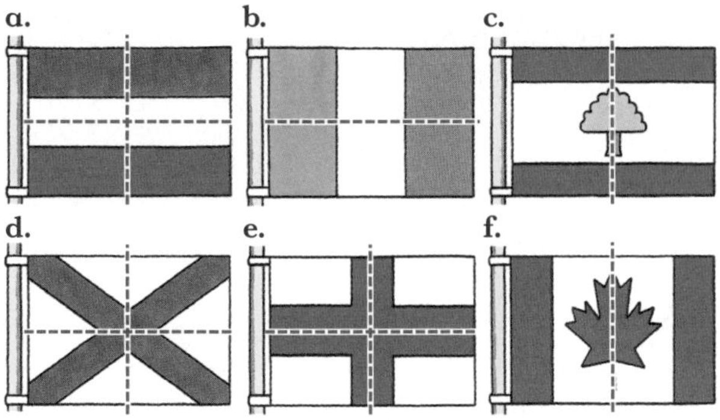

2

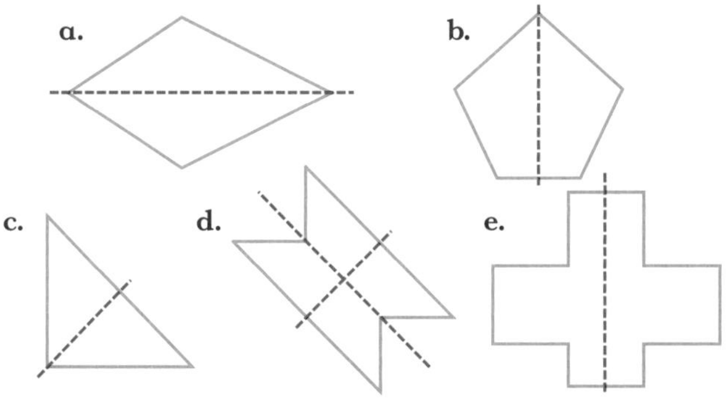

Let's try this!
Draw the lines of symmetry.

9.2 Complete a symmetrical picture

1

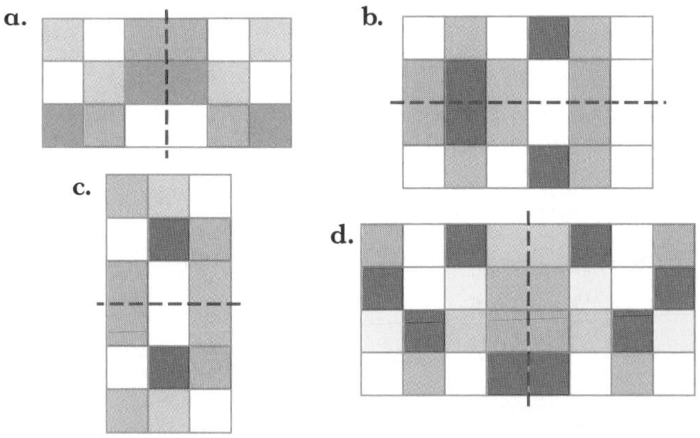

2

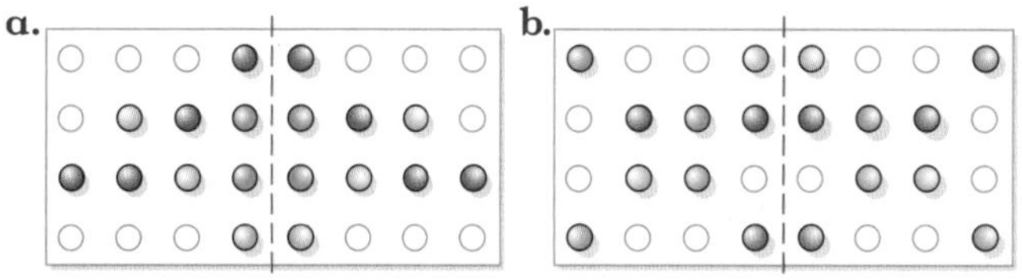

3

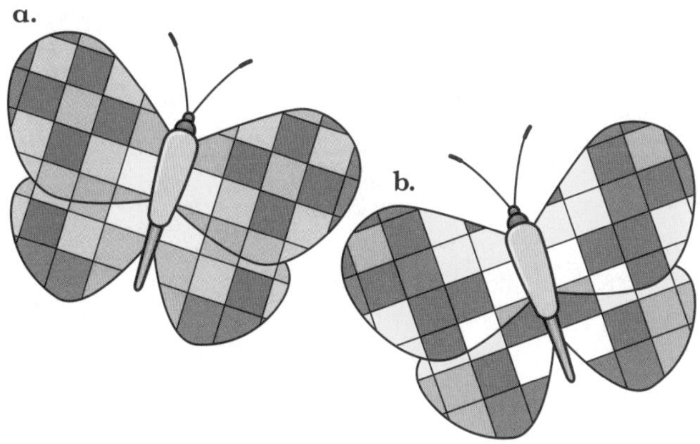

Let's try this!
Draw the lines of symmetry.

9.3 Repeating patterns of shapes

1 **a.** Continue the pattern with beads.
b. Continue the pattern with shapes.

2 Continue the patterns.

3

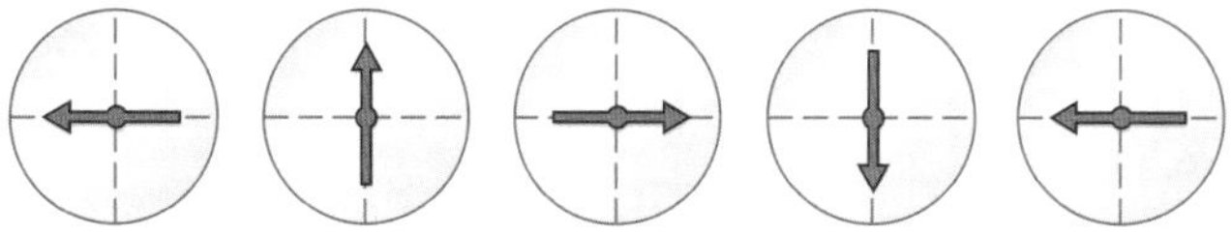

Let's try this!
Fill in the missing patterns.

9.4 The way home

1 **a. Holly's route**
Forward 2.
Turn left.
Forward 4.
Turn right to house 1.

Jimmy's route
Forward 2.
Turn right.
Forward 3.
Turn left to house 8.

b. Karl lives at No. 10
Turn right.
Forward 5.
Turn left.
Forward 2 to bus stop.

Leone lives at No. 4
Turn left.
Forward 1.
Turn right.
Forward 2 to bus stop.

2 Forward 2.
Turn left.
Forward 1.
Turn right.
Forward 4.
Turn left.
Forward 3.

3 Answers may vary.

Let's try this!
Answers may vary.

9.5 In position
1 **a.** Bolts **b.** Hammer **c.** Screws **d.** Tacks
e. Scissors **f.** Screws **g.** Saw

2

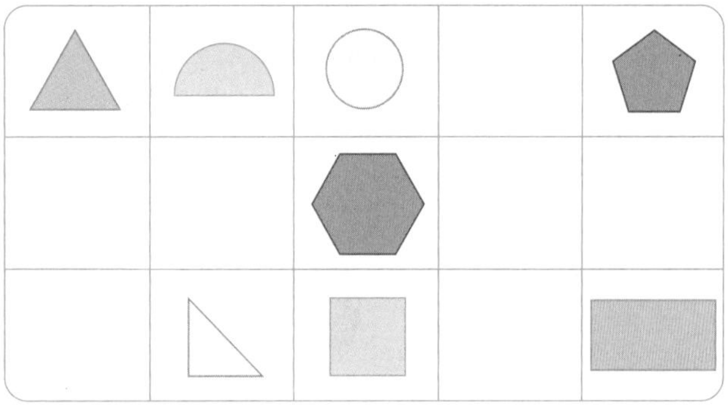

Let's try this!
Answers may vary.

Chapter 10 Measure – Weight, Capacity and Time

10.1 Market stall weights
1 Answers may vary.

2 Answers may vary.

3 The apples are **lighter** than 1 kg.
The peaches are **heavier** than 1 kg.
The cherries are **lighter** than 1 kg.
The apples are **lighter** than the peaches.
The peaches are **heavier** than the cherries.

4 **a.** 2 kg **b.** 5 kg **c.** 4 kg **d.** 3 kg

Let's try this!
a. 4 kg **b.** 2 kg **c.** 1 kg

10.2 Market scales
1 Compare your drawing with your partner's drawing.

2 **a.** 5 kg **b.** 3 kg **c.** 10 kg

3 **a.** $3\frac{1}{2}$ kg **b.** $8\frac{1}{2}$ kg **c.** $5\frac{1}{2}$ kg **d.** 9 kg
e. $6\frac{1}{2}$ kg **f.** $7\frac{1}{2}$ kg

Let's try this!

Vegetable	1 box	2 boxes	4 boxes
Carrots	5 kg	10 kg	20 kg
Onions	8 kg	16 kg	32 kg
Potatoes	10 kg	20 kg	40 kg

10.3 Calculating capacities
1 **a.** C **holds less** than A. B **holds more** than D.
b. A = 5 C = 4 B = 3 D = 2
c. C holds double **D**. D + B hold the same as **A**.
A + **D** together hold the same as **B** + C.

2 **a.** A full kettle holds **3** litres of water.
b. If you fill the teapot with water from the kettle there will be **1** litre of water left in the kettle.
c. 1 litre makes **5** cups of tea. 3 litres makes **15** cups of tea.
4 litre makes **20** cups of tea. 5 litres makes **25** cups of tea.

3 **a.** 2 litre tin and 1 litre tin.
b. 4 litre tin and 1 litre tin; two 2 litre tins and a 1 litre tin; one 2 litre tin and three 1 litre tins
c. 4 litre tin and 2 litre tin; a 4 litre tin and two 1 litre tins; three 2 litre tins; two 2 litre tins and two 1 litre tins; one 2 litre tin and four 1 litre tin.
d. 4 litre tin, 2 litre tin and a 1 litre tin; a 4 litre tin and three 1 litre tins; three 2 litre tins and a 1 litre tin; two 2 litre tins and three 1 litre tins; a 2 litre tin and five 1 litre tins

Let's try this!
Some possible combinations:
$10l = 4l + 4l + 2l$; $4l + 2l + 2l + 2l$; $2l + 2l + 2l + 2l + 2l$

10.4 Litres and half litres
1 **a.** Jug A = $2l$, Jug B = $3l$, Jug C = $4l$, Jug D = $5l$
b. A to E Mark up to the correct level.

2 **a.** $2\frac{1}{2}\,l$ **b.** $1\frac{1}{2}\,l$ **c.** $4\frac{1}{2}\,l$ **d.** $3\frac{1}{2}\,l$ **e.** $6\frac{1}{2}\,l$
f. $9\frac{1}{2}\,l$ **g.** $5\frac{1}{2}\,l$ **h.** $8\frac{1}{2}\,l$

3 **a.** $2\frac{1}{2}\,l$ **b.** $6\,l$ **c.** $4\frac{1}{2}\,l$

Let's try this!
$5l + 4l = 9l$ $5l + 3l + 1l = 9l$ $4l + 3l + 2l = 9l$

10.5 Days, weeks and months
1 **a.** 1st Monday 2nd Tuesday 3rd Wednesday
4th Thursday 5th Friday 6th Saturday
7th Sunday
b. Rome: Friday 5 June
New York: Sunday 7 June
Cape Town: Tuesday 2 June

2 1. January
2. February
3. March
4. April
5. May
6. June
7. July
8. August
9. September
10. October
11. November
12. December

3 **a.** June comes after May.
b. February comes after January.
c. May comes after April.
d. November comes before December.
e. September comes after August.

Let's try this!
Answers may vary.